# THE VERSALOG
## SLIDE RULE

## An Instruction Manual

by

**E. I. FIESENHEISER, B.S. M.S. C.E.**

*Professor of Civil Engineering*

*with chapters on*

CIVIL ENGINEERING APPLICATIONS

*by*

E. I. FIESENHEISER, B.S., M.S., C.E.

MECHANICAL ENGINEERING APPLICATIONS

*by*

R. A. BUDENHOLZER, B.S., M.S., PH.D.

*Professor of Mechanical Engineering*

ELECTRICAL ENGINEERING APPLICATIONS

*by*

B. A. FISHER, B.S., M.S., E.E.

*Associate Professor of Electrical Engineering*

*All at* ILLINOIS INSTITUTE *of* TECHNOLOGY

THE FREDERICK POST COMPANY
CHICAGO

# INTRODUCTION

## YOUR VERSALOG SLIDE RULE

Early in 1950, a group of prominent professors and practicing engineers were approached with the problem of designing a practical slide rule for *today's* problems. They were asked to examine every existing concept of slide rule practice in the light of modern-day specialized needs and to develop a new slide rule that would be the ultimate in efficiency and practical usefulness.

This is the story of your new VERSALOG Slide Rule . . . designed by engineers . . . for engineers. Not merely an instrument of mathematics . . . the VERSALOG is designed around the problems of *engineering*. It provides both the practicing engineer and the student with a far more efficient and helpful, up-to-date "tool" to match the high tempo of present day engineering development

## INSTRUCTION TEXT

In this discussion of the VERSALOG Slide Rule, the authors break with conventional "instruction pamphlets." The value of their approach will be appreciated by students, teachers, and practicing engineers who have experienced difficulty in the transition between the abstract mathematical approach of contemporary slide rules and "instructions" . . . and the practical application of those mathematical principles to every day engineering problems.

In addition to offering a very readable treatment of slide rule fundamentals, the designers of the VERSALOG make a long step forward toward the *complete* use of the slide rule and *all* its scales by graphically illustrating the application of your VERSALOG to three separate and distinct engineering fields. Each section presents a practical and easy-to-comprehend guide to the use of the VERSALOG in these specialized fields. By so doing, the authors and editors of this text, eminently qualified authorities in the fields of Civil, Electrical, and Mechanical Engineering, have solved one of the great problems of slide rule technique and use.

# CONSTRUCTION

While many things are sought for in a slide rule, one is foremost above all others . . . unquestioned accuracy at all times, no matter what the conditions. The owner and user of the VERSALOG Slide Rule will be gratified to know that the ultimate in craftsmanship, care and exactness in manufacture has been followed to produce the very finest, most accurate slide rule sold today.

To insure accuracy, your VERSALOG Slide Rule is constructed from carefully selected and laminated bamboo. Bamboo is tough, and was chosen because of its ability to resist contraction and expansion under varying climatic conditions. Bamboo has natural oils, imperceptible to the touch, constantly lubricating the bearing surfaces and allowing a smoothness of action not found in any other wood or metal. Years of use make it operate more easily. White celluloid faces are used for easy reading and all scale graduations and figures are deeply machine cut into the face to insure a lifetime of accurate calculations.

In your POST VERSALOG SLIDE RULE, you have truly one of the finest and most exact instruments this century's ingenuity is able to produce.

THE FREDERICK POST COMPANY

Our deepest gratitude is extended to Professor E. I. Fiesenheiser, Professor R. A. Budenholzer, and Associate Professor B. A. Fisher for their efforts throughout the designing and developing stages of the VERSALOG rule, also for the writing and edification of this text book of instructions.

It is a tribute to the engineering profession, and to the never ending efforts of those men who are devoting their lives educating and training the engineer of the future.

# PREFACE

The professional engineer or the engineer in training is to be congratulated for having purchased a slide rule. Among computing tools there is no other which contributes more to speed and efficiency and to reducing the labor of involved calculations. The Post Versalog Slide Rule is among the finest of such computing instruments. Its design is the result of much study and of many consultations with a panel of engineering teachers who practice engineering and represent major engineering fields. While this rule will be of use to other professional people such as scientists, accountants and mathematicians, it was designed primarily with the needs of the engineer in mind.

Every effort has been made to select a wide range of the most useful scales and to arrange these logically and conveniently. An adequate scale designation system with a consistent coloring scheme has been provided for the trigonometric scales. These improvements, devised by Professor B. A. Fisher, will be appreciated by users of the slide rule. Four log log and four reciprocal log log scales have been provided instead of the usual three of each, thus extending the range of numbers. The convenient, symmetrical arrangement of these log log scales should be regarded as a definite improvement.

An soon as the student engineer acquires the slide rule he should devote time to study of the instrument. Such time and effort will be rewarded by increased efficiency and accuracy and fewer errors during examinations. He should practice to develop mastery of *all* of the scales and their most *efficient* uses. Not to do so is to handicap himself. Learning to use only one or two scales is like owning an expensive new automobile which one drives around only in low gear, either not realizing that there are higher gears, or failing to let the mechanism shift into high for smooth speedy operation.

This instruction manual has been written for study without the aid of a teacher. However, a knowledge of basic elementary mathematics is assumed. The student engineer will probably have this knowledge when he acquires the slide rule. Although the manual contains many examples of mathematical problems as well as engineering problems, no effort is made to teach either mathematics or engineering in this book.

Ideas and thoughts of others will be found intermingled with those of the author. Grateful acknowledgment is therefore made to the following: Mr. Walter G. Hollmann, Director of Research for the Frederick Post Company; Mr. Herman Ritow, Consultant; other teachers and writers; and to students in the classroom.

E. I. Fiesenheiser

Chicago, Illinois
*Feb. 1951*

# TABLE OF CONTENTS

# THE VERSALOG SLIDE RULE

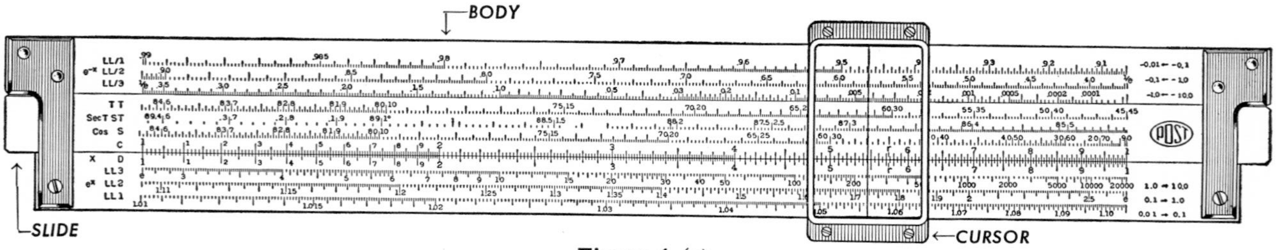

Figure 1 (a)

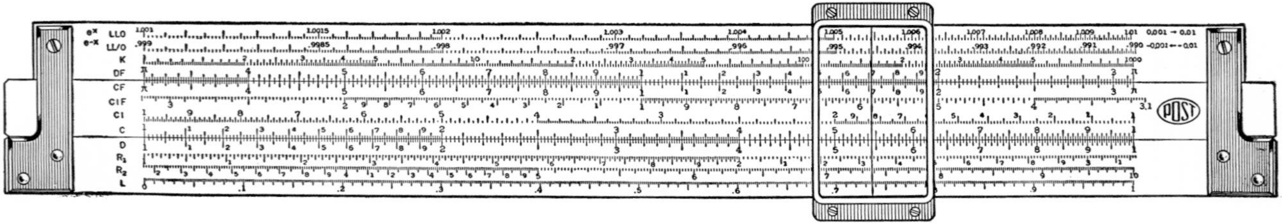

Figure 1 (b)

# *Chapter 1*

## DESCRIPTION, ADJUSTMENT, CARE AND MANIPULATION OF THE SLIDE RULE

In the study of this chapter, the reader should have the slide rule before him and should refer to Fig. 1 (a) and (b), in which the various parts of the rule are indicated.

**General Description.** The slide rule consists essentially of 3 parts: the body, or fixed part; the slide, which slides in grooves in the body; and the cursor, with the hairline in the center. Scales appear on both the body and the slide, and on both sides of the rule. This means that either one or the other, or both sides, may be used in making a calculation.

The body and slide are constructed of laminated bamboo with an overlay of white plastic. This type of construction insures against warpage and provides unusual dimensional stability so that the rule will be accurate and operate smoothly over a wide range of weather conditions.

**Adjustment.** Your Versalog slide rule should come to you in perfect adjustment. However, in case it is dropped or severely jarred, the precise adjustment may be lost. In any case it is advisable to check the adjustment occasionally to make sure that the scale readings are as accurate as the instrument will allow. In order to check and adjust the slide rule the following procedure may be followed.

With the rule held so that the shorter body member is uppermost, move the slide until the C and D scales coincide perfectly. The DF scale on the upper body member should now be in alignment with the identical CF scale of the slide. If it is not, the upper body member must be moved to right or left. In order to adjust this member, loosen the two screws in the metal end bars by about one-half turn and move the upper body member until the DF scale coincides with the CF scale, then tighten the screws.

The hairline should now be moved to coincide with the left index (the 1 mark) of the D scale. In this position the hairline should also coincide with the symbol $\pi$ of the DF scale. If it does not, the hairline is not perpendicular to the slide rule scales. It must be adjusted so that it coincides with the ends of both D and DF scales. It may be adjusted,

1

if necessary, by loosening the four screws of the metal cursor frame which surrounds the glass. The glass may then be moved until perfect alignment is obtained, and the screws carefully retightened.

The rule may now be turned over for examination of the hairline adjustment on the reverse side. The hairline should be in perfect alignment with the left index of the D scale as well as with the 1/e mark of the LL/3 upper scale. If it is not, this hairline must be moved. This is done again by loosening the four screws of the metal cursor frame, moving the glass, and retightening the screws. When properly set, both hairlines should align simultaneously. In making this adjustment care must be exercised not to disturb the position of the hairline previously adjusted.

In case it is difficult to push the slide, the body parts may be gripping it too tightly. To adjust for easy operation, loosen a screw at one end *only* on the adjustable part of the body. This end may then be pulled away from the slide. The screw may then be retightened and the operation repeated at the other end. By adjustment of one end at a time the alignment of the scales is not affected. One of the properties of the bamboo wood construction is that the operation of the slide becomes easier and smoother with age and usage.

**Care of Your Versalog Slide Rule.** It is important to keep the slide rule as clean as possible. Keeping the hands clean and keeping the rule in its case when not in use will help. To clean the scales a slightly moist cloth may be used. To remove particles from under the glass of the cursor, a narrow strip of paper may be cut and placed over the scales. The cursor may then be run over the paper, pressing down on the cursor at the same time. This will cause the dirt particles to adhere to the strip of paper.

**Manipulation.** In setting the hairline the cursor is generally pushed with one hand to the neighborhood of the desired setting. It may then be set accurately by placing the thumbs of both hands against either side of the cursor frame, pushing a little more with one thumb than the other to set the hairline.

In setting the slide it may be moved to the neighborhood of the desired setting with one hand. Usually one end of the slide projects beyond the body of the rule. Should the right end project, the right hand is then used to make the exact setting. The thumb and forefinger of the hand grasp the slide and at the same time press against the end of the body of the rule. By this control an exact setting of the slide may be made very quickly, the forefinger and thumb doing the precise work. In case the left end of the slide projects, the left hand is used in the same manner to make the setting.

The above methods of manipulation are those used by the writer but it is realized that the student may develop his own methods. Those given, therefore, should be regarded merely as suggestions from one who has learned to use the instrument.

# Chapter 2

## THE SCALES OF THE SLIDE RULE

This chapter contains a brief description of the scales and how to read them. Much more information concerning the scales and their uses is given in later chapters. This discussion, however, should provide the student with a background and a general acquaintance with the slide rule.

**Scale Descriptions.** The Post Versalog Slide Rule has 23 scales, located and arranged in a convenient and logical manner. These scales will permit the solution of *any kind* of arithmetical problem except adding and subtracting. Each scale is designated on the rule by a letter or a combination of letters and symbols which appears at the left end of the scale. All of the scales (except the L scale) are logarithmic, which means that the distances along the scales are proportional to the logarithms (to the base 10) of the numbers or functions represented.

Probably the scales most often used are those marked C and D. For convenience these appear on both sides of the rule. They are identical in markings and length, the D scale appearing on the body, and the C scale appearing on the movable slide. The scale length is 25 cm. or 9.84 in. This is slightly less than 10 in. although the instrument is commonly called a 10 inch slide rule. The scale equation is $x = 9.84 \log_{10} N$, where x is the distance in inches from the left end to any number N appearing on the scale. The C and D scales are used for multiplication and division and in conjunction with all of the other scales on the rule.

The CI scale, on the slide, is exactly the same as the C and D scales, except that it is graduated and numbered from right to left. Its use for rapid, efficient multiplication and division is explained in a later chapter. Numbers appearing on the CI, inverted scale, are reciprocals of numbers directly opposite on the C scale.

The DF, folded scale, located on the body of the rule, is of the same construction and length as the D scale, but begins and ends at $\pi$. This places the 1 mark very near the mid point of the scale. The convenience of this arrangement for rapid work and for certain types of calculations is explained later. The CF scale is identical to the DF scale but is located on the slide. The CIF scale is identical to the CF scale, except that it is numbered and graduated from right to left, and numbers on the CIF scale are reciprocals of those directly opposite on CF.

The L scale is used to obtain common logarithms (to the base 10). When the hairline is set to any number on the D scale, the mantissa of its common log is read at the hairline on the L scale. Since the D scale is logarithmic, the L scale is an ordinary, uniformly divided, or natural scale.

The $R_1$ and $R_2$ scales are used for obtaining squares and square roots directly. When the hairline is set on any number on an R scale, its square appears at the hairline on the D scale.

The K scale is used for obtaining cubes and cube roots directly. When the hairline is set to a number on the D scale, its cube appears at the hairline on the K scale.

The log log scales LL0, LL1, LL2, and LL3 are called the LL scales and are used to obtain powers and roots of numbers from 1.001 to 22,000. Fractional and decimal powers are easily handled with these scales. Powers of e (the base of natural logarithms) are also obtained directly on the LL scales by setting the hairline to the power desired on the D scale. For the log log scales the scale equation is $x = 9.84(\log_{10}\log_e N_2 - \log_{10}\log_e N_1)$ in which x is the distance in inches between numbers $N_1$ and $N_2$ appearing on *any* LL scale.

The scales designated LL/0, LL/1, LL/2, and LL/3 are called the reciprocal log log scales and are used in the same manner as are the LL scales, but for numbers less than 1. These are also log log scales and the same scale equation applies to them. Their range extends from 0.00005 to 0.999 and the numbers and graduations extend from right to left. When the hairline is set to a number on the D scale, the reciprocal of e raised to the power of this number is read directly on a reciprocal log log scale.

The log log scales are in reality one-quarter lengths of a single long scale. For example each of the LL scales is 25 cm. in length, equal to one-fourth of a meter. The numbering of the LL0 scale begins at 1.001 and ends at 1.01; LL1 begins at 1.01 and ends at 1.105; LL2 begins at 1.105 and ends at e; and LL3 begins at e and ends at 22,000. If these four scales could be placed end to end, a single scale one meter in length would result.

An important property of the log log (LL) scales is that they represent powers designated $e^x$ whereas the reciprocal log log scales represent reciprocals $1/e^x$, which are the same as $e^{-x}$. Hence any number on an

LL scale has its reciprocal directly opposite on the corresponding reciprocal log log scale. For example, the reciprocal of a number on LL1 is directly opposite on LL/1 and the reciprocal of a number on LL2 is directly opposite on LL/2. It will be noted that reciprocals of numbers close to 1 may be obtained with extreme accuracy. Many of the other advantages and uses of the log log scales will be explained in a later chapter.

The Cos S scale is used to obtain sine and cosine functions of angles and is graduated in degrees and decimals of degrees. With the hairline set at the angle on the S scale the sine of the angle is read on the C scale. For sines the scale is graduated from left to right from 5.74 degrees to 90 degrees. To obtain the cosine of an angle the hairline is set at the angle on the Cos scale and its cosine function is read on the C scale. For cosines the scale is graduated from right to left from zero to 84.3 degrees.

The T scale is used to obtain the tangent of angles from 5.71 degrees to 84.3 degrees. For angles in the range of 5.71 degrees to 45 degrees this scale is graduated from left to right. When the hairline is set to an angle in this range, its tangent function is read on the C scale. For angles from 45 degrees to 84.3 degrees the hairline is set at the angle and its tangent is read at the hairline on the CI scale. In this range the scale is graduated from right to left.

An additional scale marked Sec T ST is provided for determining the tangent function of small angles varying from 0.57 to 5.73 degrees. This scale is graduated from left to right in this range and is used with the C scale. It may also be used for determining the sine function of small angles since if the angle is small sine and tangent functions are nearly equal. For large angles the scale is numbered and graduated from right to left for use with the CI scale. In the range of 84.27 to 89.43 degrees, with the hairline set to the angle on this scale, either tangents or secants are read at the hairline on the CI scale. In this range the tangent and the secant are nearly equal.

More detailed explanations for the trigonometric scales are given in Chapter 6 on "Trigonometric Operations."

**Reading the Scales.** The construction and reading of the D scale only will be explained here, since with this information the student will be able to read any of the other scales. In Fig. 2 a logarithmic curve is shown. The abscissa of any point on the curve is a number N while the ordinate of the same point is the common logarithm of N. On the D scale the figures 1 to 10 represent the numbers N, whereas the distance from the end of the scale to any number N is proportional to $\log_{10}N$. Since the curve is not a straight line the scale is not uniformly divided. For example, the distance from 1 to 2 on the rule is 9.84 $\log_{10}2 = 2.96$ in. whereas the distance from 2 to 3 is 9.84 $(\log_{10}3 - \log_{10}2) = 1.74$ in.

Since the distance between 1 and 2 on the D scale is relatively long, it was possible to divide this distance into 10 major

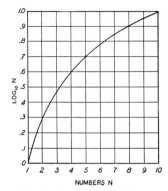

Fig. 2—Logarithmic Curve.

lengths, to subdivide each of these major lengths into 2 secondary lengths, and in turn to subdivide each of these into 5 tertiary lengths. All of the distances between division marks are proportional to the differences of logarithms of the numbers represented. The shortest distance between tertiary divisions is still great enough so that the eye is not confused in reading the scale. In fact it is possible to set the fine hairline by eye at a point *between* the smallest division marks, estimating its location to the nearest tenth of the length for very accurate settings. Hence settings of 4 digit accuracy may be made for numbers whose first digit is 1. In Fig. 3 four different hairline readings are given, each to 4 significant digits. The readings which the operator would take from the slide rule are shown directly above each long vertical line.

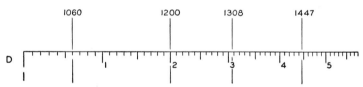

Fig. 3—D Scale Readings.

Between numbers 2 and 3 and also between numbers 3 and 4 on the D scale, the distance is divided into 10 major lengths, each of which is subdivided into 5 secondary lengths. Again the hairline may be set by eye between the smallest division marks. Settings of 3 to 4 digit accuracy may therefore be made on this part of the scale.

For the remainder of the scale, for example, between numbers 4 and 5, 10 major divisions are provided, each space being subdivided into

2 secondary lengths. The hairline may be set by eye between the smallest division marks with precision, to give 3 digit accuracy for numbers whose first digit is 4, 5, 6, 7, 8, or 9. In Fig. 4 five different hairline readings are given.

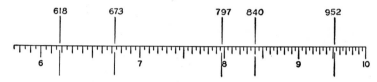

**Fig. 4—D Scale Readings.**

**Accuracy.** The left end of the D scale, for numbers having 1 as the first digit, is accurate to 4 significant figures whereas the right end of the scale is accurate only to 3 significant figures. Since both ends are used, the accuracy as a whole is limited to 3 significant figures. Such accuracy is all that is required for ordinary design calculations.

**Effects of Errors in Reading the Scale.** In case the hairline is set incorrectly or the reading is made incorrectly, the effect may be evaluated by use of the scale equation previously stated as $x = 9.84 \log_{10} N$, in which x is the distance in inches from the left end of the scale to any number N appearing on the scale. Taking the derivative of both sides with respect to N, the following equation results: $\dfrac{dN}{N} = 2.3026\left(\dfrac{dx}{9.84}\right)$. The term $\dfrac{dN}{N}$ is the relative error in the number N, while $\dfrac{dx}{9.84}$ is the relative error in reading or setting the hairline. Therefore the relative error in the number is independent of the size of the number or its location on the scale and is 2.3026 times the relative error in reading the scale.

## *Chapter 3*

## MULTIPLICATION AND DIVISION

Multiplication and division are performed on the slide rule by the simple process of adding or subtracting logarithms. The logarithm of the product of two numbers is equal to the sum of the logarithms of the numbers; the logarithm of the quotient of two numbers is equal to the difference of their logarithms. Since the scales used are logarithmic scales, products and quotients are obtained automatically simply by setting the numbers directly opposite, one on a scale of the body, the other on a scale of the slide.

**Multiplication Using Lower Scale Combinations.** In Fig. 5 the D and the CI scales are used to multiply 2 by 4. The D scale is on the lower part of the body and the CI scale is on the lower part of the slide. Hence the D and CI scale combination is called a *lower scale combination*. (To avoid confusion only the scales being used are shown in Fig. 5 and in the figures which follow.) The addition of log 2 and log 4 to

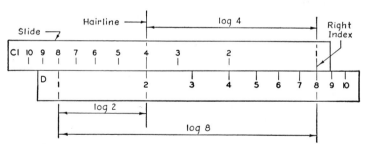

**Fig. 5—Use of D and CI Scale Combination for Efficient
Multiplication of 2 by 4.**

obtain log 8 is shown. The distances along the scales are proportional to the logarithms of the numbers. This is the reason why adding these distances automatically adds the logarithms.

In this operation the hairline is used by setting it to the number 2 on the D scale. The slide is then moved until the number 4 on the CI scale coincides with the hairline. The answer 8 is read on the D scale opposite the 1 mark, which is the right index of the CI scale. It is unnecessary to move the hairline again, since the answer is read by a glance of the eye to the right index of the slide.

The multiplication of 2 by 4 might have been performed *less efficiently* by using the C and D scales as shown in Fig. 6. By this method the hairline is set on 2 of the D scale; the slide is moved until the 1 mark or left index of the C scale coincides with the hairline; then the hairline is

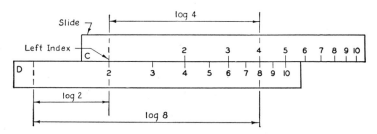

Fig. 6—D and C Scale Combination Used Inefficiently to Multiply 2 by 4.

moved to 4 on the C scale in order to read the result 8 at the hairline on the D scale. This method of multiplication requires two movements of the hairline instead of one and ordinarily requires a much greater movement of the slide. It is not recommended for use in multiplication since it is wasteful of time and energy.

Multiplication should always start by setting the hairline to a number on a D scale. The slide should then be moved until the other number on a CI scale coincides with the hairline. The product is then read on a D scale by glancing at the index of the slide. (A D scale may be either D or DF, a CI scale either CI or CIF.)

The multiplication of 2 by 4 in Fig. 5 required a slide movement to the *left* so that the answer was read at the *right* index of the slide. The

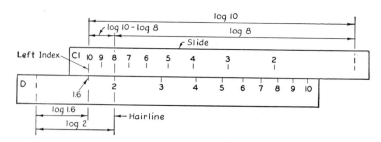

Fig. 7—D and CI Scale Combination for Multiplying 2 by 8.

multiplication of two numbers such as 2 and 8 requires a movement of the slide to the *right* so that the answer is read at the *left* index of the slide, as in Fig. 7. The hairline is set on 2 of the D scale and the number 8 on the CI scale is moved to the hairline. Here it is noted that the scale length $\log 2 - (\log 10 - \log 8) = \log \dfrac{2(8)}{10} = \log 1.6$, whereas we know that the product of 2 and 8 is 16. Hence the result 1.6 is correct except for the decimal point. We do not use the slide rule to determine a decimal point anyhow because a rough calculation easily locates the decimal point. Therefore the product 16 is read on the D scale at the *left* index of the slide.

A point to emphasize is that either the left or the right index, whichever is in contact with the D scale, is used to read the result on the D scale.

**Division using Lower Scale Combinations.** In dividing two numbers a D and C scale combination should be used for the most efficient operation. Dividing involves subtracting logarithms. The example of Fig. 8 indicates the division of 9 by 6. In this case $\log 9 - \log 6 = \log 1.5$. The slide has been moved to the *right*. Therefore the quotient 1.5 is read on the D scale at the *left* index of the C scale.

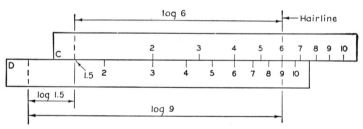

Fig. 8—D and C Scale Combination for Dividing 9 by 6.

Another example is shown in Fig. 9 in which 1.8 is divided by 2.5. The hairline is set to 1.8 on the D scale. Then 2.5 on the C scale is moved to the hairline. The result 0.72 is read on the D scale at the *right* index of C since the slide was moved to the *left*. From the figure the scale distances are as follows: $\log 1.8 + \log 10 - \log 2.5 = \log \dfrac{1.8(10)}{2.5} = \log 7.2$. The figure 7.2 is correct except for the location of the decimal point. This is located by mental calculation since dividing 1.8 by 2.5 obviously results in a number less than 1.

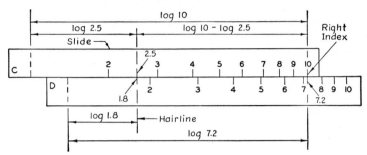

**Fig. 9—D and C Scale Combination for Dividing 1.8 by 2.5.**

**Use of the Upper Group of Scales.** There is an upper group of scales designated DF, CF, and CIF. The DF scale is on the upper part of the body; the CF and CIF scales are on the upper part of the slide. These scales may also be used for multiplying and dividing since they are identical in construction to the D, C and CI scales, except that the index of each is very near the middle of each scale. The letter F indicates that these are folded scales, beginning and ending at points other than 1. The symbol $\pi$ appears at the left end of the DF scale. This symbol should be directly opposite the number 1 of the D scale. (Check this by setting the hairline over $\pi$ on the DF scale.) It is easy to multiply by $\pi$. Simply set the hairline on a number on the D scale and read $\pi$ times the number on DF. For example, setting the hairline on 2 of the D scale, we read 6.28 on DF. Since the DF scale begins with log $\pi$, by moving the hairline a scale distance of log 2, we are adding log $\pi$ to log 2. Since log $\pi$ + log 2 = log $2\pi$, the product $2\pi$ = 6.28 is read on DF at the hairline.

The same relationship exists on the slide with the C and CF scale combination. With the hairline set on any number on C, we read $\pi$ times the number on CF.

Fig. 10 shows the use of the upper scales in multiplying. Here 1.1 is multiplied by 1.2 by setting the hairline to 1.1 on DF and moving 1.2 on CIF to the hairline. The product 1.32 is read on DF at the 1 mark or index of the CIF scale.

Let it be assumed that the slide was centered, with all indices in line, before beginning the calculation. From Fig. 10 the total movement of the slide from its centered position was proportional to log 1.1 + log 1.2 = log 1.32. The left index of the C scale has moved exactly the same distance, so that the answer might also be read on the D scale, at the left index of C. Hence either the DF or the D scale may be read.

The lower C and CI scales have two indices, one at each end, while the upper CF and CIF scales each have only one index, near the center. Note that wherever the slide is moved, the lower index reading on D is the same as the upper index reading on DF.

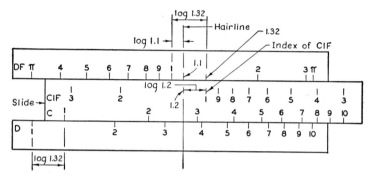

**Fig. 10—DF and CIF Scale Combination for Multiplying 1.1 by 1.2.**

For multiplying 1.1 by 1.2 there is a definite advantage in using the upper scales. The total movement of the slide from its centered position in Fig. 10 was 1.18 in. Had the D and CI scale combination been used, a slide movement of 8.66 in. would have been required. The advantage of the upper group of scales for certain operations is therefore obvious.

Division may be performed on the upper group of scales as follows: to divide 8 by 2 efficiently, set hairline to 8 on DF and move 2 on CF to hairline; read 4 on DF at index of CF, or read 4 on D at right index of C. This requires a slide movement of about 3.9 in. If the same operation were performed by using the C and D scale combination, a slide movement of about 5.9 in. would be required.

**Choice of Lower or Upper Scale Combinations.** For some operations the choice of scale combinations makes no difference in efficiency, either the upper or lower group may be chosen. For other operations a lower scale combination is more advantageous, while for still other operations an upper scale combination is best. To determine which combination is best to use, a general rule is desirable. Such a rule may be stated definitely as follows: *Either lower or upper scale combinations may be used for multiplication and division, but whenever one scale com-*

*bination requires moving the slide more than one-half its length, use the other.* By following this rule the maximum slide movement required is one-half of 9.84 in. or about 5 in.

The student should perform the following exercises in multiplication and division in order to familiarize himself with the six scales and their most efficient uses. A mental calculation or a few rough figures set down on paper will serve to locate decimal points. No attempt should be made to read results more accurately than the instrument allows. In this connection it will be remembered that accuracy is limited to four significant figures for numbers whose first digit is 1 but to only three significant figures for numbers beginning with the digits 2 to 9. The D and CI or the DF and CIF scale combinations should always be used when multiplying, whereas the D and C or the DF and CF scale combinations should always be used when dividing.

## EXERCISES IN MULTIPLICATION

Perform the operation and indicate the most advantageous scale combination. (Answers are given at the end of the manual for checking.)

| | | |
|---|---|---|
| 1.  2.4 × 3.02 | 7. 2.13 × 12.11 | 13. 4.15 × 26.2 |
| 2. 1.52 × 2.95 | 8. 1.49 × 1.32 | 14. 29.2 × 7.68 |
| 3. 6.12 × 3.4 | 9. 9.12 × 8.25 | 15. 20.8 × 95.7 |
| 4. 1.57 × 2.2 | 10.  7.1 × 9.6 | 16. 42.5 × 14.24 |
| 5. 3.24 × 7.22 | 11. 5.13 × 9.08 | 17. 2.25 × 3720 |
| 6. 9.18 × 3.32 | 12.  3.3 × 9.8 | 18. 392 × 10.33 |

## EXERCISES IN DIVISION

Perform the operation and indicate the most advantageous scale combination.

| | | |
|---|---|---|
| 19. 9.3 ÷ 3.08 | 25. 9.3 ÷ 2.18 | 31. 9.3 ÷ 6.5 |
| 20. 8.55 ÷ 2.96 | 26. 8.55 ÷ 10.5 | 32. 8.55 ÷ 5.12 |
| 21. 7.48 ÷ 2.63 | 27. 7.48 ÷ 115 | 33. 7.48 ÷ 3.54 |
| 22. 6.3 ÷ 0.27 | 28. 6.3 ÷ 14.2 | 34. 6.3 ÷ 7.5 |
| 23. 450 ÷ 19.2 | 29. 450 ÷ 10.4 | 35. 450 ÷ 57.2 |
| 24. 1950 ÷ 435 | 30. 1950 ÷ 94.5 | 36. 1950 ÷ 10.6 |

**Multiplying or Dividing a Series of Numbers.** A great advantage in slide rule calculation is that any number of factors may be multiplied together in one continuous operation to obtain their product. In terms of logarithms, the addition of the logarithms of a series of numbers is equal to the logarithm of the product of the numbers. If more than two factors are to be multiplied together, the logarithms of the first two are added automatically on the slide rule scales and to this sum the logarithm of the next factor is added by the next setting, to this sum is added the logarithm of the next factor, and so on, for any number of factors. Therefore it is *not* necessary, as in long hand multiplication, to multiply the factors two by two and then to multiply these separate products. A simple example will serve to illustrate the procedure:

$$1.41 \times 7.25 \times 2.02 \times 8.1 = 167.3$$

In order to obtain the product 167.3 by slide rule we set the hairline on 1.41 on the D scale, move 7.25 on CI to the hairline, move the hairline to 2.02 on C, and move 8.1 on CI to the hairline. The product 167.3 is read on the D scale at the left index of C. Only the final result needs to be set down on paper. About thirty seconds are required to do the entire operation. By either long hand or electric calculator multiplication we would first multiply 1.41 by 7.25 to obtain 10.2225; then we would multiply 2.02 by 8.1 to obtain 16.362; then 10.2225 would be multiplied by 16.362 to obtain 167.2605450. The numbers 10.2225 and 16.362 would need to be set down on paper or transferred to another dial, even if a calculator were used. Of course the final result 167.2605450 is accurate to ten significant figures. However, in ordinary design calculations such accuracy is unnecessary and time is therefore wasted in doing unnecessary work. Our slide rule result 167.3 is accurate to four significant figures, a degree of accuracy usually sufficient.

On the slide rule, division is just as easy as multiplication. In fact, to divide by a number we need only multiply by its reciprocal. Due to the presence of the reciprocal or "I" scales as well as the others we may choose the most convenient scale to perform either multiplication or division when a series of factors is involved. It will be well to keep in mind that in multiplying one must add logarithms and that in dividing one must subtract logarithms. By noting, always, the direction of the numbering and graduations of the scales one plans to use, errors will be avoided. A number of examples follow, illustrating the use of the scales in combined multiplication and division. The student should work through these examples and check the results.

$3.25 \times 4.28 \times 9.13 = 127$

**Operations**

Set hairline to 3.25 on D.
Move 4.28 on CI to hairline.
Move hairline to 9.13 on CF.
Read 127 on DF at hairline.

$4.7 \times 5.24 \times 10.12 = 249$

**Operations**

Set hairline to 4.7 on D.
Move 5.24 on CI to hairline.
Move hairline to 10.12 on C.
Read 249 on D at hairline.

$$\frac{6.45 \times 7.51}{8.26} = 5.86$$

**Operations**

Set hairline to 6.45 on DF.
Move 7.51 on CIF to hairline.
Move hairline to 8.26 on CIF.
Read 5.86 on DF at hairline.

Performing the operations in this way first adds the log 6.45 to the log 7.51, then subtracts log 8.26, the result being log 5.86.

It is also possible to do the work as follows:

Set hairline to 6.45 on D.
Move 8.26 on C to hairline.
Move hairline to 7.51 on C.
Read 5.86 on D at hairline.

(This method first subtracts log 8.26 from log 6.45, then adds log 7.51.)

It is believed that fewer errors result by first using all factors in the numerator, then next using all factors in the denominator. In this way one first concentrates on continuous multiplication, then on continuous division, without alternating from one process to the other. Therefore the first method given for solving the last example is preferred.

$$\frac{120 \times 8.25 \times 19.1 \times 9.6}{40.5 \times 3.24 \times 50.4 \times 25} = 1.098$$

**Operations**

Set hairline to 120 on D.
Move 8.25 on CI to hairline.
Move hairline to 19.1 on C.
Move 9.6 on CI to hairline.
Move hairline to 40.5 on CI.
Move 3.24 on C to hairline.
Move hairline to 50.4 on CI.
Move 25 on C to hairline.
Read 1.098 on D at left index of C.

$$\frac{30.6 \times 41.2 \times 5.41}{(40.8)^2 \times 7.3} = 0.561$$

**Operations**

Set hairline to 30.6 on D.
Move 41.2 on CI to hairline.
Move hairline to 5.41 on C.
Move 40.8 on C to hairline.
Move hairline to 40.8 on CI.
Move 7.3 on C to hairline.
Read 0.561 on D at right index of C.

$$\frac{100 \times (60.5)^3}{48 \times 3(10)^4 \times 655} = 0.0235$$

### Operations

Set hairline to 60.5 on DF.
Move 60.5 on CIF to hairline.
Move hairline to 60.5 on C.
Move 48 on C to hairline.
Move hairline to 3 on CI.
Move 655 on C to hairline.
Read 0.0235 on D at hairline.

The decimal point may be located by a rough calculation by setting down the numbers rounded off, and using a cancellation process, thus

$$\frac{10\cancel{0}x\cancel{6}\cancel{0}x6\cancel{0}x6\cancel{0}}{5\cancel{0}x\cancel{3}x1\cancel{0}\cancel{0}\cancel{0}\cancel{0}x700} = \frac{72}{3500} = \frac{7.2}{350}$$

We observe that 7.2 is divided by a number greater than 100 but less than 1000. Therefore the result is a number less than 0.072 but greater than 0.0072. The slide rule gives us the three significant figures 235, so that the result must be 0.0235.

## EXERCISES IN MULTIPLICATION AND DIVISION OF A SERIES OF FACTORS

37. $12.1 \times 2.36 \times 4.25$

38. $5.72 \times 6.25 \times 7.13$

39. $7.48 \times 802 \times 920$

40. $\dfrac{2.2}{7.25}$

41. $\dfrac{8.24 \times 9.13}{10.12 \times 14.7}$

42. $\dfrac{7.85 \times 204 \times 82.6}{6.55 \times 101.5 \times 71.9}$

43. $\dfrac{18.6}{4.1 \times 3.64 \times 2.04}$

44. $\dfrac{1}{1.04 \times 1.71 \times 9.25}$

45. $\dfrac{1080}{(29.4)^2 \times 7.6}$

46. $\dfrac{(21.2)^2 \times 8.95}{17.6 \times 61.7 \times 4.6}$

**Multiplication or Division of a Single Factor by a Series of Numbers.** In engineering calculations it is frequently necessary to obtain the products of several different numbers each multiplied by the same single factor. In this type of problem the best procedure is to set the index of the C scale to the single factor on the D scale and to use the D and C or the DF and CF scale combination for multiplying. By this method only the hairline needs to be moved to perform the successive multiplications. Suppose, for example, 1.27 is to be multiplied in turn by 3.16, 4.28, 6.55, 8.4, and 9.85:

> Set the left index of C to 1.27 on D.
> Move hairline to 3.16 on C, reading 4.01 on D.
> Move hairline to 4.28 on C, reading 5.44 on D.
> Move hairline to 6.55 on C, reading 8.32 on D.
> Move hairline to 8.4 on CF, reading 10.67 on DF.
> Move hairline to 9.85 on CF, reading 12.51 on DF.

*Division* of a single factor by a series of numbers is illustrated by the following example. Suppose 41.5 is to be divided in turn by 12.4, 20.8, 44.5, and 92. For this work it is best to use the reciprocal scales CI and CIF for division:

> Set right index of CI to 41.5 on D.
> Move hairline to 12.4 on CI, reading 3.35 on D.
> Move hairline to 20.8 on CI, reading 1.995 on D.
> Move hairline to 44.5 on CIF, reading 0.933 on DF.
> Move hairline to 92 on CIF, reading 0.451 on DF.

In setting an index of the slide in the above operation, *either* the left *or* the right index of the slide might have been used. It should be remembered, however, that the slide need not be moved more than one-half of the scale length. The number 3.16 of the D scale is located approximately at its mid point. Therefore *for a single factor less than 316, set the left index; for one greater than 316, set the right index of the* slide. If this rule is followed the single factor may be either *multiplied* or *divided* by *any* number without again moving the slide. It is only necessary to move the hairline to perform the successive operations.

## EXERCISES

47. Multiply 320 successively by 1.15, 2.42, 3.18, 4.5, 5.42, 6.88, 7.96, 8.05, and 9.6.
48. Divide 7.18 successively by 1.02, 2.15, 3.29, 4.18, 5.67, 6.41, 7.85, 8.76, and 9.34.

**Proportion.** The principle of proportion is convenient in solving simple equations without having to solve the equations explicitly for the unknown. The use of proportion in this manner is perhaps best illustrated by the use of simple algebraic expressions. Let x be the unknown quantity which is to be solved for when the known quantities are C′, D′, C, or D. In a proportion such as $\frac{x}{C'} = \frac{D}{C}$, C′, D, and C are known and x is to be determined. If we set the number D on a D scale (D or DF) opposite C on a C scale (C or CF), x may be read directly on the D scale opposite C′ on the C scale. For example, to solve for x in $\frac{x}{25} = \frac{24.4}{41.5}$, set 24.4 on D opposite 41.5 on C; opposite 25 on C, read x = 14.7 on D.

In an expression such as $\frac{D'}{x} = \frac{D}{C}$, set D on a D scale opposite C on a C scale and read x on the C scale opposite D′ on the D scale. As an example, to solve for x in $\frac{39.8}{x} = \frac{14}{71}$, set 14 on DF opposite 71 on CF. Now opposite 39.8 on D, read x = 202 on C.

### EXERCISES

By use of the principle of proportion, solve the following examples:

49. $\frac{x}{6.45} = \frac{9000}{16700}$

50. $\frac{x}{12.1} = \frac{21.4}{195}$

51. $\frac{7.18}{x} = \frac{32.4}{17.9}$

52. $\frac{18.25}{x} = \frac{71}{705}$

53. $\frac{356}{51} = \frac{42.5}{x}$

**Solution of the Quadratic Equation by Factoring.** If any quadratic equation is transformed into the form $x^2 + Ax + B = 0$, the roots or values of the unknown x may be determined by a simple method, using the slide rule scales. We let the correct roots be $-x_1$ and $-x_2$. By factoring, $(x + x_1)(x + x_2) = 0$. The terms $-x_1$ and $-x_2$ will be the correct values of x providing the sum $x_1 + x_2 = A$ and the product $x_1.x_2 = B$. An index of the CI scale may be set opposite the number B on the D scale. With the slide in this position, no matter where the hairline is set, the product of simultaneous CI and D scale readings or of simultaneous CIF and DF scale readings is equal to B. Therefore it is only necessary to move the hairline to a position such that the sum of the simultaneous CI and D scale readings, or the sum of the simultaneous CIF and DF scale readings, is equal to the number A.

As an example, the equation $x^2 + 10x + 15 = 0$ will be used. We set the left index of CI opposite the number 15 on the D scale. We then move the hairline until the sum of CI and D scale readings, at the hairline, is equal to 10. This occurs when the hairline is set at 1.84 on D, the simultaneous reading on CI being 8.15. The sum $x_1 + x_2 = 1.84 + 8.15 = 9.99$, sufficiently close to 10 for slide rule accuracy. Roots or values of x are therefore $-x_1 = -1.84$ and $-x_2 = -8.15$. Obviously the values of x solving the equation $x^2 - 10x + 15 = 0$ will be $+1.84$ and $+8.15$ since in this case A is negative, equal to $-10$.

As a second example the equation $x^2 - 12.2x - 17.2 = 0$ will be used. The left index of CI is set on 17.2 on the D scale. Since this number is actually negative, $-17.2$, and since it is the product of $x_1$ and $x_2$, obviously one root must be positive, the other negative. Also the sum of $x_1$ and $x_2$ must equal $-12.2$. We therefore move the hairline until the sum of simultaneous scale readings is equal to $-12.2$. This occurs when the hairline is set on 13.5 on the DF scale, the simultaneous reading at the hairline on CIF being 1.275. $x_1$ is therefore $-13.5$ and $x_2$ is 1.275, since $x_1 + x_2 = -13.5 + 1.275 = -12.225$, sufficiently close to $-12.2$ for slide rule accuracy. The values of x solving the equation are therefore $-x_1 = 13.5$ and $-x_2 = -1.275$.

### EXERCISES

Solve the following quadratic equations for values of x:

54. $x^2 - 34.53x + 18 = 0$.
55. $x^2 - 21.14x + 32 = 0$.
56. $x^2 - 20.2x - 120 = 0$.
57. $2x^2 + 82.8x + 840 = 0$.
58. $1.2x^2 - 13.38x + 36 = 0$.

# Chapter 4

## SQUARE ROOT AND SQUARES, CUBE ROOT AND CUBES

**Square Root and Squares.** The Post Versalog Slide Rule is equipped with two root scales, $R_1$ and $R_2$. These scales are used with the D scale to obtain square roots directly with considerable accuracy. If the hairline is set to any number on the D scale, the square root of the number is read at the hairline on $R_1$ or $R_2$. For convenience the $R_1$ and $R_2$ scales are located on the body of the rule directly below the D scale. The $R_1$ and $R_2$ scales are component parts of a single long scale 50 cm. in length. $R_1$, 25 cm. long, is graduated and numbered from left to right from 1 to $\sqrt{10}$, while $R_2$, also 25 cm. long, is graduated and numbered from left to right from $\sqrt{10}$ to 10.

The root scales are also used to obtain squares of numbers. For numbers between 1 and $\sqrt{10}$ (equal to 3.162), if the hairline is set at the number on $R_1$, its square is read at the hairline on D. For numbers between 3.162 and 10, if the hairline is set at the number on $R_2$, its square is read at the hairline on D.

The simple mathematical relationship of the R and D scales may be expressed as follows: $R^2 = D$. Taking logarithms of both sides of the equation, $2 \log R = \log D$. Therefore the scale distance, from the index to any number on the R scale is twice the scale distance to the same number on the D scale. This means that readings of the R scales are *twice* as accurate as readings of the D scale.

Examples in the use of the square root scales follow:

| | |
|---|---|
| $\sqrt{9} = 3$ | $\sqrt{90} = 9.49$ |
| **Operations** | **Operations** |
| Set hairline to 9 on D. Read 3 on $R_1$ at hairline. | Set hairline to 90 on D. Read 9.49 on $R_2$ at hairline. |

| | |
|---|---|
| $\sqrt{250} = 15.81$ | $\sqrt{4120} = 64.2$ |
| **Operations** | **Operations** |
| Set hairline to 250 on D. Read 15.81 on $R_1$ at hairline. | Set hairline to 4120 on D. Read 64.2 on $R_2$ at hairline. |

$$\sqrt{57,500} = 239.8$$

**Operations**

Set hairline to 57,500 on D.
Read 239.8 on $R_1$ at hairline.

$$\sqrt{605,000} = 778$$

**Operations**

Set hairline to 605,000 on **D**.
Read 778 on $R_2$ at hairline.

---

$$\sqrt{2,720,000} = 239.8$$

**Operations**

Set hairline to 2,720,000 on D.
Read 1649 on $R_1$ at hairline.

---

It will be observed that whenever the number has an *odd* number of digits its square root appears on $R_1$ and whenever the number has an *even* number of digits its square root appears on $R_2$.

As in all the previous examples, the square root of a number larger than 1 is smaller than the number. However, the square root of a number smaller than 1 will be greater than the number. This type of problem is illustrated by the following examples:

$$\sqrt{0.05} = 0.2236$$

**Operations**

Set hairline to 0.05 on D.
Read 0.2236 on $R_1$ at hairline.

$$\sqrt{0.5} = 0.707$$

**Operations**

Set hairline to 0.5 on D.
Read 0.707 on $R_2$ at hairline.

---

$$\sqrt{0.0005} = 0.02236$$

**Operations**

Set hairline to 0.0005 on D.
Read 0.02236 on $R_1$ at hairline.

$$\sqrt{0.005} = 0.0707$$

**Operations**

Set hairline to 0.005 on D.
Read 0.0707 on $R_2$ at hairline.

---

$$\sqrt{0.000005} = 0.002236$$

**Operations**

Set hairline to 0.000005 on D.
Read 0.002236 on $R_1$ at hairline.

$$\sqrt{0.00005} = 0.00707$$

**Operations**

Set hairline to 0.00005 on D.
Read 0.00707 on $R_2$ at hairline.

From the above examples it is apparent that when the number of zeros to the right of the decimal point is *odd,* the square root is read on the $R_1$ scale. When the number of zeros to the right of the decimal point is *even,* the square root of the number is read on the $R_2$ scale. Also when there are *no* zeros to the right of the decimal point the square root is read on $R_2$.

In squaring a number we set the number on the $R_1$ or $R_2$ scale and read its square on the D scale. The number of digits in the result is easily determined. The square of a number set on $R_1$ will have an odd number of digits, while the square of a number set on $R_2$ will have an even number of digits. For example, in squaring 350 we set the hairline to 350 on $R_2$, hence the square will have an even number of digits. On D we read the figures 1225. Since the number 350 has three digits, its square will have six digits, an *even* number. The square is therefore 122,500. Other examples follow:

$$(250)^2 = 62,500$$

### Operations

Set hairline at 250 on $R_1$.

(Result will have an odd number of digits, one less than twice the number being squared.)

Read 62,500 on D at hairline.

---

$$(4.5)^2 = 20.25$$

### Operations

Set hairline on 4.5 on $R_2$.
(Result will have even number of digits.)
Read 20.25 on D at hairline.

---

$$(1,748)^2 = 3,060,000$$

### Operations

Set hairline at 1748 on $R_1$.
(Result will have odd number of digits.)
Read 3,060,000 on D at hairline.

$$(682)^2 = 465,000$$

## Operations

Set hairline at 682 on $R_2$.
(Result will have even number of digits.)
Read 465,000 on D at hairline.

In squaring a given number less than 1 occurring on $R_1$, the number of significant zeros in the result will be twice those in the given number plus one zero. For any given number occurring on $R_2$ the square will have exactly twice the number of significant zeros as the given number. For example:

$$(0.169)^2 = 0.0286$$

## Operations

Set hairline to 0.169 on $R_1$.
(Result will have odd number of zeros to the right of the decimal point.)
Read 0.0286 on D at hairline.

---

$$(0.043)^2 = 0.00185$$

## Operations

Set hairline to 0.043 on $R_2$.
(Result will have even number of zeros to the right of the decimal point.)
Read 0.00185 on D at hairline.

---

**Areas of Circles.** One decided advantage of the root scales is that areas of circles may be obtained simply by setting the hairline to the radius of the circle on $R_1$ or $R_2$. The area may then be read on the DF scale at the hairline. No slide movement is required. Since the area of a circle is $\pi R^2$ the value of $R^2$ on the D scale is multiplied by $\pi$ when the DF scale is read. For example, the area of a circle whose radius is 0.375 is obtained by setting the hairline at 0.375 on $R_2$ and reading 0.442 at the hairline on DF.

## EXERCISES

Perform the indicated operations using $R_1$, $R_2$, and D scales:

59. $\sqrt{6}$

60. $\sqrt{27}$

61. $\sqrt{925}$

62. $\sqrt{1,265}$

63. $\sqrt{71,500}$

64. $\sqrt{820,000}$

65. $\sqrt{1,970,000}$

66. $\sqrt{51,000,000}$

67. $(20.4)^2$

68. $(715)^2$

69. $(1,070)^2$

70. $(125.4)^2$

71. $(0.85)^2$

72. $(0.094)^2$

73. $(0.0076)^2$

74. $(0.000157)^2$

75. $\sqrt{0.424}$

76. $\sqrt{0.0875}$

77. $\sqrt{0.00725}$

78. $\sqrt{0.00094}$

79. Calculate the areas of circles whose radii are 0.125, 0.1875, 0.25, 0.3125, 0.4375, 0.5.

**Cube Root and Cubes.** The K scale is the cube scale of the slide rule. With the hairline set on a number on the D scale, its cube may be read at the hairline on the K scale. If the cube root of a number is desired, the hairline is set at the number on K and the cube root is read at the hairline on D. These two scales are of equal length. Mathematically, since $D^3 = K$ and $\log D = \dfrac{\log K}{3}$, the K scale is divided into three equal segments, each segment graduated and numbered from left to right. The first segment extends from 1 to 10, the second from 10 to 100, and the third from 100 to 1,000. Since the scale distance from the index to a number on K is only one-third the scale distance to the same number on D, the accuracy of K scale readings is only one-third that of the D scale readings.

The most efficient use of the K and D scale combination is achieved by observing the location of the decimal point. Since the three segments of the K scale are graduated and numbered between ranges 1 to 10, 10 to 100 and 100 to 1,000, the operator should have no difficulty in placing the decimal point for numbers between 1 and 1,000. However, for numbers less than 1 or greater than 1,000 the decimal point may be moved both before and after the operation to obtain a number within the range of the scales. In such cases a definite rule may be followed: If the decimal point is moved n number of places in a number set on D, it must be moved back 3n places in the cube, which is read on K; or if the decimal point is moved n number of places in a number set on K, it must be moved back $\frac{n}{3}$ places in the cube root, which is read on D. For example, to cube 0.456 we move the decimal point one place to the right. By setting the hairline at 4.56 on D we obtain 95 at the hairline on K. We now move the decimal point *back* three places to the left to obtain 0.095. Other examples follow:

$$(0.0325)^3 = 0.0000343$$

### Operations

Move decimal point two places to the right.

$$(3.25)^3 = 34.3$$

Move decimal point back six places to the left.
Result is then 0.0000343

---

$$(1{,}214)^3 = 1{,}790{,}000{,}000$$

### Operations

Move decimal point three places to the left.

$$(1.214)^3 = 1.79$$

Move decimal point back nine places to the right.
Result is 1,790,000,000.

---

$$\sqrt[3]{0.0052} = 0.173$$

### Operations

Move decimal point three places to the right.

$$\sqrt[3]{5.2} = 1.73$$

Move decimal point back one place to the left.
Result is 0.173.

$$\sqrt[3]{26{,}400} = 29.8$$

## Operations

Move decimal point three places to the left.

$$\sqrt[3]{26.4} = 2.98$$

Move decimal point back one place to the right.
Result is 29.8.

---

### EXERCISES

Perform the indicated operations using the K and D scales:

80. $\sqrt[3]{6}$

81. $\sqrt[3]{24}$

82. $\sqrt[3]{270}$

83. $\sqrt[3]{1{,}720}$

84. $\sqrt[3]{29{,}000}$

85. $\sqrt[3]{560{,}000}$

86. $(3.2)^3$

87. $(41)^3$

88. $(750)^3$

89. $\sqrt[3]{0.32}$

90. $\sqrt[3]{0.041}$

91. $\sqrt[3]{0.0075}$

92. $(0.245)^3$

93. $(0.036)^3$

94. $(0.0048)^3$

## *Chapter 5*

### OPERATIONS INVOLVING POWERS, RECIPROCALS, EXPONENTIAL EQUATIONS, LOGARITHMS. USES OF THE LOG LOG AND THE LOG SCALES

The log log scales are exceptionally useful in engineering calculations which involve powers and exponents. As previously explained, square roots and squares, cube roots and cubes, may be found by using the special scales $R_1$, $R_2$, and K. However, *any* power or root of a number may be found by using the log log scales. For numbers close to one, powers and roots are determined in this way with considerable accuracy.

One important feature of the log log scales is that the decimal point is always given by the scale reading, so that it is unnecessary to determine its location by additional calculation. This feature reduces the chance for error. However, because of frequent changes in sub-dividing along the scales and because of the extremely wide range of numbers (from 0.00005 to about 22,000), care must be used in reading the scales. The sub-dividing should be carefully checked by eye for that portion of any log log scale being used.

**Powers of e and Reciprocals.** The numbers on the log log scales represent powers of e. Since all of the log log scales are located on the body of the rule and are used with the D scale, the powers are read by simply setting the hairline. If x represents a number to which the hairline is set on the D scale, values of $e^x$ appear at the hairline on the log log scales. LL0, LL1, LL2, and LL3 (called the LL scales) are used for positive powers of e; whereas LL/0, LL/1, LL/2, and LL/3 (called the reciprocal log log scales) are used for negative powers of e. To aid the operator in remembering this relationship the symbol x appears at the left end of the D scale, the symbol $e^x$ at the left end of the LL scales, and $e^{-x}$ at the left end of the reciprocal log log scales.

The scales are arranged symmetrically about the horizontal center line of the rule. The arrangement is in the order of LL3, LL2, LL1 below and LL/3, LL/2, LL/1 above, from the center line outward on one face of the rule. Turning the rule over, LL0 and LL/0 appear at the top. The log log scales have black and the reciprocal log log scales red numbering.

The relationship of successive scales is that of one-tenth powers of e. For example, if we set the hairline to the number 2 on D, we read $e^2 = 7.4$ on LL3, $e^{0.2} = 1.2215$ on LL2, $e^{0.02} = 1.0202$ on LL1, and $e^{0.002} = 1.002$ on LL0. Since $e^2 = (e^{0.2})^{10}$, 1.2215 is the one-tenth power of 7.4. With the hairline set at 2 on D we may also read $e^{-2} = 0.135$ on LL/3, $e^{-0.2} = 0.8187$ on LL/2, $e^{-0.02} = 0.9802$ on LL/1, and $e^{-0.002} = 0.9980$ on LL/0. Thus eight different powers of e are obtained with one setting of the hairline.

To aid in reading powers of e on the log log scales, symbols have been provided opposite the right ends, indicating the range of x covered by each scale. The arrows indicate the directions of scale numberings.

Since $e^{-x}$ is the reciprocal of $e^x$, any number on an LL scale has its reciprocal directly opposite on the corresponding reciprocal log log scale. In the above example the reciprocal of 7.4 is therefore 0.135 and the reciprocal of 1.2215 is 0.8187, etc. In determining reciprocals in this manner the decimal point is always given by the scale reading.

### EXERCISES

Determine the following powers of e:

95. $e^5$, $e^{0.4}$, $e^{0.03}$, $e^{0.008}$.
96. $e^{-4}$, $e^{-0.9}$, $e^{-0.074}$, $e^{-0.0056}$.

Determine reciprocals of the following numbers by use of the log log scales:

97. 8,500, 750, 64, 8.5, 0.951, 0.0754, 0.0056, 0.00014.

**Hyperbolic Functions.** The functions $\sinh x = \frac{1}{2}(e^x - e^{-x})$, $\cosh x = \frac{1}{2}(e^x + e^{-x})$, and $\tanh x = \frac{e^{2x} - 1}{e^{2x} + 1}$ may be determined by substituting the powers of e read from the log log scales. For example, $\sinh 0.434 = \frac{1}{2}(1.544 - 0.648) = 0.448$; $\cosh 0.434 = \frac{1}{2}(1.544 + 0.648) = 1.096$; and $\tanh 0.434 = \frac{2.382 - 1}{2.382 + 1} = 0.408$. Values $e^x = e^{0.434} = 1.544$ and $e^{-x} = e^{-0.434} = 0.648$ were taken from the LL2 and LL/2 scales by only a single setting of the hairline to 0.434 on the D scale; $e^{2x} = e^{0.868} = 2.382$ was read on LL2 with the hairline set at 0.868 on the D scale.

### EXERCISES

Determine values of the following hyperbolic functions:

98.  sinh 0.2                        101. tanh 0.35
99.  sinh 3.0                        102. tanh 2.1
100. cosh 0.45

The inverse of the hyperbolic functions may also be evaluated by use of the log log scales. If the value of a hyperbolic function such as sinh x, cosh x, or tanh x is given or known, the value of x may then be found by substituting the known value into the formulas given below; in which A, B, or C are known:

$$\text{If sinh } x = A, \text{ then } e^x = A + \sqrt{A^2 + 1.}$$
$$\text{If cosh } x = B, \text{ then } e^x = B + \sqrt{B^2 - 1.}$$
$$\text{If tanh } x = C, \text{ then } e^x = \sqrt{\frac{1 + C}{1 - C}}.$$

The recommended procedure is to first substitute the known values into the formulas, thus solving for $e^x$. (The $R_1$ and $R_2$ scales are extremely convenient for this work.) Then set the hairline to $e^x$ on the appropriate log log scale and read x at the hairline on the D scale. For example, if sinh x is given as 2.12, x may be evaluated as follows: since $A = 2.12$, $A + \sqrt{A^2 + 1} = 2.12 + \sqrt{4.50 + 1} = 4.46$. Now setting the hairline to 4.46 on LL3, we read $x = 1.496$ at the hairline on D.

### EXERCISES

Evaluate x, given the following values of the hyperbolic functions:

103. sinh x = 9.82                   106. cosh x = 1.32
104. sinh x = 0.625                  107. tanh x = 0.917
105. cosh x = 3.73                   108. tanh x = 0.300

**Powers of Numbers.** Raising numbers to powers by using log log scales is as simple as multiplication. Distances along the log log scales are proportional to $\log_{10}\log_e N$ where N is any number appearing on a log log scale. Now if we wish to raise a number N to the exponent p to obtain $N^p$, we must add the $\log_{10} p$ by use of one of the scales on the slide, either C, CI, CIF, or CF. In equation form this operation would appear as follows:

| Setting on log log scale | Setting on slide | Reading on log log scale |
|---|---|---|

$$\log_{10}\log_e N + \log_{10} p = \log_{10} p . \log_e N = \log_{10}\log_e N^p.$$

The addition of the logarithm of the exponent p to the base 10 results in $\log_{10}\mathrm{Log}_e N^p$. For example, to raise 1.002 to the exponent 2, we set the hairline to 1.002 on LL0, move 2 on CI to the hairline, move the hairline to the right index of CI, and read 1.004 at the hairline on LL0. In this example, N corresponds to the number 1.002 and p to the exponent 2. We have added $\log_{10}2$ to $\log_{10}\log_e 1.002$ because the distance moved by the hairline from 2 to the right index of CI was proportional to $\log_{10}2$. The result is $\log_{10}\log_e(1.002)^2 = \log_{10}\log_e 1.004$. Hence, $(1.002)^2 = 1.004$. Other examples follow:

$$(1.00555)^{1.72} = 1.00957$$

### Operations

Set hairline at 1.00555 on LL0.
Move 1.72 on CI to hairline.
Move hairline to right index of CI.
At hairline read 1.00957 on LL0.

---

$$(1.00555)^{17.2} = 1.0998$$

### Operations

As above, except that the reading is taken from the LL1 scale. Since readings on LL1 are tenth powers of readings directly opposite on LL0 and the exponent 17.2 is ten times the exponent 1.72, it was necessary to read the LL1 scale. Other powers of 1.00555 may also be read with the hairline in the same position. $(1.00555)^{172} = 2.589$, read on LL2; and $(1.00555)^{1720} = 13,500$, read on LL3.

---

$$(650)^{0.5} = 25.5$$

### Operations

Set hairline at 650 on LL3.
Move right index of C to hairline.
Move hairline to .5 on C.
Read 25.5 at hairline on LL3.

$$(650)^{0.005} = 1.0329$$

## Operations

As above, except read LL1 to obtain 1.0329.

---

$$(0.99646)^{1.54} = 0.99456$$

## Operations

Set hairline at 0.99646 on LL/0.
Move 1.54 on CI to hairline.
Move hairline to right index of CI.
At hairline read 0.99456 on LL/0.

---

$$(0.554)^{8.65} = 0.0060$$

## Operations

Set hairline at 0.554 on LL/2.
Move right index of C to hairline.
Move hairline to 8.65 on C.
At hairline read 0.0060 on LL/3.

---

$$(0.00016)^{0.54} = 0.0089$$

## Operations

Set hairline at 0.00016 on LL/3.
Move right index of C to hairline.
Move hairline to 0.54 on C.
At hairline read 0.0089 on LL/3.

---

$$(0.9435)^{22.2} = 0.275$$

## Operations

Set hairline at 0.9435 on LL/1.
Move right index of C to hairline.
Move hairline to 22.2 on C.
At hairline read 0.275 on LL/3.

Negative powers of numbers may be obtained by the use of reciprocals. Remembering that $N^{-p} = \dfrac{1}{N^p}$, we may use the operations necessary to determine $N^p$, then by reading the corresponding reciprocal scale, $N^{-p}$ is obtained. For example, suppose we wish to find $25^{-0.67}$. We set the hairline at 25 on LL3, then move the right index of C to the hairline. Now moving the hairline to 0.67 on C, the result would be $25^{0.67}$ if the LL3 scale were read. However, by reading LL/3 at the hairline, the negative power $25^{-.67} = 0.116$ is obtained.

## EXERCISES

Determine the following powers of numbers:

109. $(1.00164)^{3.2}$
110. $(1.0446)^{2.54}$
111. $(1.95)^{2.7}$
112. $(31)^{0.845}$

113. $(0.99325)^{0.75}$
114. $(0.922)^{4.1}$
115. $(0.568)^{9.1}$
116. $(0.114)^{0.252}$

117. $(415)^{-.75}$
118. $(1.31)^{-3.2}$
119. $(0.877)^{-2.5}$
120. $(0.99245)^{-1.2}$

**Exponential Equations.** Equations of the form $N^p = A$, in which N and A are known quantities, may be solved for the unknown exponent p. The problem may be stated thus: to what exponent p must N be raised so that the result is A? Steps in the process may be described as follows: (1) set the hairline to the number A on a log log scale; (2) set an index of CI or of CIF to the hairline; (3) move the hairline to the number N on a log log scale; (4) read the exponent p on CI or CIF, whichever one was used in step (2). This process is the reverse of that used for determining powers of numbers. Examples follow.

$$(25.5)^p = 17.5$$

### Operations

Set hairline to 25.5 on LL3.
Move right index of C to hairline.
Move hairline to 17.5 on LL3.
At hairline read p = 0.884 on C.

$$(2.4)^p = 185$$

### Operations

Set hairline to 2.4 on LL2.
Move right index of C to hairline.
Move hairline to 185 on LL3.
At hairline read p = 5.97 on C.

## EXERCISES

Solve for the exponent p in the following equations:

121. $(9.1)^p = 16.4$                123. $(0.915)^p = 0.614$
122. $(3.25)^p = 71.5$              124. $(0.425)^p = 0.0174$

**Logarithms of Numbers.** Common logarithms (logarithms to the base 10) may be found directly by use of the L scale. If the hairline is set to a number on the D scale, the mantissa of the common logarithm of the number may be read on the L scale. Both D and L scales are located on the body of the rule, hence no slide movement is required. The characteristic of the logarithm must be determined mentally, keeping in mind that $\log_{10}1$ is zero, $\log_{10}10$ is 1, $\log_{10}100$ is 2, etc. Any number between 1 and 10 will therefore have a characteristic of 0 and any number between 10 and 100 will have a characteristic of 1, etc.

Example 121, above, may be solved by the use of the L scale, although not as easily or quickly as when the log log scales are used as previously explained. Since $(9.1)^p = 16.4$, we may equate the logarithms of both sides of the equation to obtain $p.\log_{10} 9.1 = \log_{10} 16.4$, or

$$p = \frac{\log 16.4}{\log 9.1} = \frac{1.215}{0.959} = 1.267.$$

In the above example the hairline was set to 16.4 on D and the number 0.215 was read at the hairline on L. Since 16.4 is a number whose magnitude is between 10 and 100, a characteristic of 1 was supplied to obtain the complete logarithm 1.215. The logarithm of 9.1 was read as 0.959 on L, opposite the setting of 9.1 on D. The division of 1.215 by 0.959 was performed as a separate operation using the CF and DF scales to obtain $p = 1.267$.

The log log scales are so constructed that logarithms to *any* base may easily be determined. By this method complete logarithms including both characteristic and mantissa are obtained directly. Let a number "a" represent the base of logarithms which is to be used. Mathematically then, $a^p = N$ or $p = \log_a N$, where the exponent or logarithm p is to be determined for number N to the base "a". Taking logarithms of both sides to the base e, we obtain $p.\log_e a = \log_e N$ or $p = \dfrac{\log_e N}{\log_e a}$. The numerator $\log_e N$ is determined by setting the hairline to the number N on a log log scale, the numerator then appearing directly opposite on the D scale. The denominator appears directly opposite the base "a" set on a log log scale. To obtain p the $\log_e N$ is simply divided by $\log_e a$.

As an example, in the expression $\log_{10} 9.1$, the base a = 10. Setting the hairline to 10 on LL3, the index of CF is set to the hairline. The hairline is then moved to 9.1 on LL3 and $\log_{10} 9.1 = 0.959$ is read at the hairline on CF.

$\log_{10} 800$ may be determined as follows: with the slide in the same position as before, move the hairline to 800 on LL3 and read 2.90 at the hairline on CF. This is not as accurate a result as can be obtained on the L scale where the more exact mantissa 0.903 may be read. Since the characteristic must be 2, the complete logarithm to the base 10 is 2.903.

To obtain logarithms, for example, to the base 8, we may set the index of CF opposite 8 on LL3. Moving the hairline to a number on an LL scale, its logarithm to the base 8 is read at the hairline on CF. For example $\log_8 200 = 2.55$.

In case many computations of the above type are to be made it will be advantageous to remove the slide and to reinsert it reversed. This will make it unnecessary to turn the rule over during the computations.

**Use of the Log Log Scales for the Solution of Compound Interest Problems.** An interesting and useful property of the log log scales is their application to compound interest calculations. The relationships are expressed mathematically by the following equation:

$$V = P\left(1 + \frac{r}{k}\right)^{kn}$$

In this equation V represents the value of an investment after n years have passed and P is the principal sum, initially invested at an annual rate of interest r, compounded k times each year.

As an example suppose we wish to determine the value of a Government "E" War Savings Bond at maturity, after ten years. The cost or principal invested is \$18.75 and the rate of interest paid is approximately 2.9 per cent, compounded semi-annually. The rate of interest must be divided by 100 to express per cent as a decimal. Therefore r = 0.029. Then $V = 18.75\left(1 + \dfrac{0.029}{2}\right)^{20} = 18.75(1.0145)^{20} = 18.75(1.334) = \$25.$
The value of $(1.0145)^{20}$ was obtained by setting the hairline to 1.0145 on LL1, moving the left index of C to the hairline, moving the hairline to 20 on the C scale, and reading 1.334 on LL2.

As a second example, determine the rate of interest compounded annually at which a given principal will double its value in a period of 12 years. In this case $V = 2P$ and $2P = P(1 + r)^{12}$ or $(1 + r)^{12} = 2$. Setting the hairline at 2 on LL2, we move 12 on C to the hairline. We then move the hairline to the left index of C and read $1 + r = 1.0594$ at the hairline on LL1. The rate of compound interest is therefore $r = 0.0594$ or 5.94 per cent.

**Time Credit Payments.** In installment buying the cost of an article is ordinarily paid in monthly installments, each installment consisting of the interest on the remaining unpaid balance plus an amount reducing the balance. Many people purchase homes, automobiles, furniture, and other articles by this method. The annual rate of interest is divided by the number of payments per year, which is twelve in the case of monthly payments. The following equations express the relationships:

$$P = rS\left(1 + \frac{1}{(1 + r)^n - 1}\right); \quad S = \frac{P}{r}\left(1 - \frac{1}{(1 + r)^n}\right); \quad n = \frac{\text{Log}\frac{P}{P - rS}}{\text{Log}(1 + r)}$$

in which P is the amount of each monthly payment, S is the entire sum to be paid in n monthly payments, and r is the annual interest rate.

Suppose the buyer of an automobile wishes to pay $2000 of its cost in monthly installments and has obtained a loan with an interest rate of 6 per cent. What monthly payment must be made over a period of two years in order to obtain title to the automobile?

$$r = \frac{0.06}{12} = 0.005 \text{ and } n = 2(12) = 24.$$

$$P = 0.005(2,000)\left(1 + \frac{1}{(1.005)^{24} - 1}\right) = 10\left(1 + \frac{1}{1.1270 - 1}\right)$$

$P = \$88.70$ approximately.

The value $(1.005)^{24}$ was obtained by setting the hairline to 1.005 on LL0, moving 24 on CI to the hairline, and reading 1.1270 at the hairline on LL2. The monthly payment will be approximately $88.70 for two years. The total interest paid will be $24(88.70) - 2,000 = \$128.80$.

Suppose the buyer wishes to pay $100 per month in order to retire the loan more quickly. The number of months required to pay the full amount will then be $n = \dfrac{\text{Log}\dfrac{P}{P - rS}}{\text{Log}\,(1 + r)} = \dfrac{\text{Log}\dfrac{100}{100 - 10}}{\text{Log}\,1.005} = \dfrac{0.1052}{0.00498} = 21.1,$ or approximately 21 months.

As a second example determine the loan which can be retired in one year by means of $50 monthly payments when 5 per cent interest is charged.

$$r = \frac{0.05}{12} = 0.004167$$

$$S = \frac{P}{r}\left(1 - \frac{1}{(1 + r)^n}\right) = \frac{50}{0.004167}\left(1 - \frac{1}{(1.004167)^{12}}\right)$$

$S = \$585$ which is the amount of the loan which can be paid.

# Chapter 6

## TRIGONOMETRIC OPERATIONS

**The Trigonometric Functions.** Trigonometric operations are those involving the ratios sine, cosine, tangent, cosecant, secant, and cotangent of angles. These angular functions, the reader will recall, are ratios of the lengths of the sides in a right triangle. In Fig. 11, these ratios are stated for convenient reference.

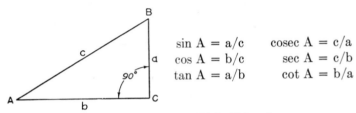

$$\sin A = a/c \qquad \text{cosec } A = c/a$$
$$\cos A = b/c \qquad \sec A = c/b$$
$$\tan A = a/b \qquad \cot A = b/a$$

Fig. 11—Parts of the Right Triangle.

The slide rule features mainly the sine, cosine and tangent functions, since these are the most commonly used by engineers. Their reciprocals, cosecant, secant, and cotangent may be determined by use of any of the reciprocal slide rule scales.

Three trigonometric scales are located on the slide. Since each scale is numbered in two directions there are actually six scales. All six graduated in degrees and decimals of degrees and are designed to be used with either the C or CI scale, depending upon whether a scale is red or black. By setting the hairline at the angle, its function is read at the hairline on C or CI. Thus the trigonometric scales may be used for multiplying or dividing by angular functions just as are the C and CI scales. Since the scales are numbered in both directions, any division mark represents both the angle and its complement. It will be remembered that the sum of an angle and its complement is 90 degrees. For example in Fig. 11 angle B is the complement of angle A.

**Coloring.** The coloring system for the numbering on the trigonometric scales is such that errors will be avoided. Angles are numbered in black when the function designated is to be read on the C scale because the C scale is black. Angles are numbered in red when the function designated is to be read on the CI scale because the CI scale is red. Hence black is used with black and red with red.

**End Zone Designations and Scale Numbering.** Scale designations are given in the left end zones in colors corresponding to the scale numbering. For all of the trigonometric scales the *order* in which the end designations are listed also corresponds to the placement of scale numbers. For example, the lower scale (nearest to the C scale) is numbered entirely in black and its black end zone designation reads Cos S. The term Cos appears first, at the *left* of the end zone, because when reading cosines the angles in degrees appear to the *left* of the division marks along the scale, for increasing angles the eye traveling from right to *left*. Conversely when reading sines, for increasing angles the eye travels from left to *right*, the angles appearing to the *right* of the division marks along the scale. Therefore the S appears at the *right* of the end zone.

The tangent (upper) scale on the slide is designated by two capital T's, the first being red, the second black. The black end designation T and the black scale numbering from left to right indicate that tangents of angles ranging up to 45 degrees are to be read directly opposite on the black C scale. The red T and red numbering from right to left, for angles greater than 45 degrees, indicate that in this range tangents are read on the red CI scale.

The above relationships repeat for the middle scale designated Sec T ST, the Sec T appearing in red for angles near 90 degrees, and whose secant and tangent functions are determined from the CI scale. The ST appears in black, for small angles whose sine and tangent functions are to be read on the black C scale.

**Decimal Point Location.** The sine varies from 0.10 to 1.0 for angles varying from 5.74 to 90 degrees, whereas the cosine varies from 1.0 to 0.10 for angles varying from 0 to 84.3 degrees. Therefore all sine and cosine functions for angles listed on the Cos S scale vary from 0.10 to 1.0.

The tangent varies from 0.10 to 1.0 for angles ranging from 5.71 to 45 degrees. Therefore for angles shown in black on the T scale, tangents read on C vary from 0.10 to 1.0. However, since tangents vary from 1.0 to 10.0 for angles between 45 and 84.29 degrees, the tangent read on CI for angles shown in red, must vary from 1.0 to 10.0.

Sines and tangents vary from 0.01 to 0.10 for angles between 0.57 and 5.73 degrees. Therefore sines or tangents of angles shown in black on ST vary from 0.01 to 0.10. However, tangents and secants vary from 10 to 100 for angles between 84.3 and 89.43 degrees. Therefore, for angles in this range, shown in red on the Sec T scale, the secant or the tangent varies from 10 to 100.

### EXERCISES

Determine the following natural functions by use of the slide rule scales:

125. sin 76°.
126. sin 54° 30' (Convert to 54.5°).
127. sin 15° 24' (Convert to 15.4°).
128. sin 0° 54' (Convert to 0.9°).
129. sin 3° 51' 36" (Convert to 3.86°).
130. cos 34.5°.
131. cos 74.7°.
132. cos 83° 30'.
133. tan 15° 42'.
134. tan 49° 18'.
135. tan 77° 30'.
136. tan 83.55°.
137. sec 89° 18'.
138. tan 88.4°.
139. tan 2° 24'.

## EXAMPLES IN THE USE OF THE TRIGONOMETRIC SCALES

In the right triangle of Fig. 12 two sides are given. Procedures for determining angles A and B and the length of side c follow:

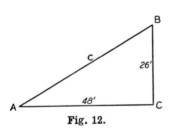

Fig. 12.

Tan A = $\frac{26}{48}$ = 0.542 from a separate operation using C and D scales. Next set the hairline to 0.542 on C and read A = 28.4° at the hairline on T. Tan B = $\frac{48}{26}$ = 1.845 from a separate operation using DF and CF scales. Next set the hairline to 1.845 on CI and read B = 61.6° at the hairline on T.

The above method is cumbersome and involves unnecessary work. A better procedure is as follows: set the right index of C at 48 on D; move the hairline to 26 on D (0.542 now appears on C at the hairline); read A = 28.4° at the hairline on T. Angle B is determined directly as 61.6°, the complement of A.

The length c may also be determined as the hypotenuse of the triangle whose two other sides are known, by taking the square root of the sums of squares of the two known sides. A quicker method, however, is to divide 26′ by the sine of the opposite angle. Thus $\dfrac{26'}{\sin A} = 54.6'$. To obtain this result, leaving the hairline at 26 on D, move 28.4° on S to the hairline; read 54.6′ on D at the right index of C.

In Fig. 13 angles A and C and side "a" are given in the obtuse triangle. Angle B and lengths b and c are to be determined. Angle B = 180° − 30° − 46° = 104°. Sin B = sin (180° − B) = sin 76°. Using the law of sines we may write the propor-

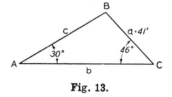

**Fig. 13.**

tion $\dfrac{a}{\sin A} = \dfrac{b}{\sin B} = \dfrac{c}{\sin C}$, or in our case $\dfrac{41'}{\sin 30°} = \dfrac{b}{\sin 76°} = \dfrac{c}{\sin 46°}$. We may now make use of the principle of proportion, previously explained in Chapter 3, to evaluate b and c. Setting the hairline to 41′ on D, we move 30° on S to the hairline. We now move the hairline to 76° on S, reading b = 79.5′ at the hairline on D. Moving the hairline to 46° on S, we read c = 59.0′ at the hairline on D.

In Fig. 14 the three sides a, b, and c are given. The angles are to be determined. Making use of the law of cosines, $\cos A = \dfrac{-a^2 + b^2 + c^2}{2bc} = \dfrac{-400 + 900 + 964}{2(30)31.05} = \dfrac{1464}{1863}$. Set the right

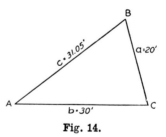

**Fig. 14.**

index of C to 1863 on D; move the hairline to 1464 on D; read A = 38.2° at the hairline on the Cos scale. Also by the law of cosines, $\cos B = \dfrac{a^2 + c^2 - b^2}{2ac} = \dfrac{400 + 964 - 900}{2(20)31.05} = \dfrac{464}{1242}$. To determine angle B we now set the left index of C to 1242 on D; move the hairline to 464 on D, and read B = 68.1° at the hairline on the Cos scale. Angle C is determined as 180° − A − B = 73.7°.

## EXERCISE

140.

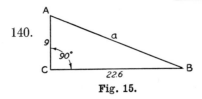

Fig. 15.

Determine angles A and B and length c.

141.

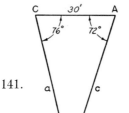

Fig. 16.

Determine lengths a and c.

142.

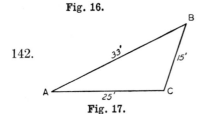

Fig. 17.

Determine angles A, B, and C.

**Combined Operations.** Calculations involving products and quotients of trigonometric functions may be performed by using the trigonometric scales without actually reading the functions from the C or CI scales. It is only necessary to remember to use any scale as a C scale when the angles are numbered black and as a CI scale when the angles are numbered red. Examples of this type of computation follow:

$$9.2 \sin 43° \cos 70.46° = 2.10$$

### Operations

Set right index of C at 9.2 on D.
Move hairline to 43° on S.
Set right index of C to hairline.
Set hairline to 70.46° on Cos.
Read 2.10 on D at hairline.

$$10.1 \tan 18.5° \tan 48° = 3.75$$

## Operations

Set left index of C at 10.1 on D.
Move hairline to 18.5° on T.
Move 48° on T to hairline.
Read 3.75 on D at right index of C.

---

$$\frac{12.8 \tan 19° \sin 47°}{\cos 25° \tan 32°} = 5.69$$

## Operations

Set left index of C at 12.8 on D.
Move hairline to 19° on T.
Set right index of C to hairline.
Move hairline to 47° on S.
Move 25° on Cos to hairline.
Set right index of C to hairline.
Move 32° on T to hairline.
Read 5.69 on D at right index of C.

---

**Vector Components and Complex Numbers.** A vector is a quantity having both magnitude and direction. In Fig. 18 a vector R is shown having a magnitude represented by its length and a direction Θ, which is the angle between the vector and the x-axis. The vector component x, in the x-direction, is equal to R cos Θ; the component y, in the y-direction, is equal to

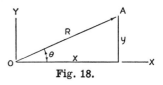

Fig. 18.

R sin Θ. These components may be determined by use of the sine and cosine scales. For example, let R = 8 and Θ = 27°. We set the right index of C at 8 on the D scale. Moving the hairline to 27° on Cos, we read x = 7.13 at the hairline on D. Moving the hairline to 27° on S, we read y = 3.63 at the hairline on D.

From the theory of complex numbers, in which $j = \sqrt{-1}$, it may be shown that $e^{j\Theta} = \cos \Theta + j \sin \Theta$. Multiplying both sides by R we obtain $R \cdot e^{j\Theta} = R \cos \Theta + j R \sin \Theta$. Here the complex number $R \cdot e^{j\Theta}$ consists of two parts, R cos Θ being the real part, j R sin Θ being the imaginary part. The number may be represented graphically in Fig. 18 by the point A whose coordinates are x and y. In the figure the x coordinate represents the real part and the y coordinate the purely imaginary part. The y-axis for the imaginary part is perpendicular to the x-axis for the real part of the complex number.

The above expression may be simplified by noting that $R \cos \theta = x$ and $R \sin \theta = y$. Then $R \cdot e^{j\theta} = x + j\,y$. The x and y values are determined as vector components of R as previously explained. This operation is called changing from exponential form to component form.

In case the complex number is expressed in component form, with x and y given, it may be changed into the exponential form if desired. The relationships are easily seen from Fig. 18. $y/x = \tan \theta$ and $R = \dfrac{y}{\sin \theta}$. As an example, consider the complex number $7.2 + j\,4.5 = R \cdot e^{j\theta}$, in which R and angle $\theta$ are to be determined:

$$\tan \theta = y/x = 4.5/7.2$$

Set right index of C to 7.2 on D.
Move hairline to 4.5 on D.
Read $\theta = 32°$ on T at hairline.

$$R = y/\sin \theta = y/\sin 32°$$

Leaving hairline at 4.5 on D.
Move 32° on S to hairline.
Read $R = 8.49$ on D at right index of C.

We now have as the result $7.2 + j\,4.5 = 8.49\,e^{j32°}$.

### EXERCISES

143. Determine the x and y components of the vector $R = 16.8$ if $\theta = 54°$.
144. Solve for x and y in the equation $21\,e^{j\theta} = x + j\,y$, if $\theta = 27°$.
145. Change the complex number $14 + j\,8.9$ to exponential form.

**Angles in Radians.** Angles in radians may be converted to angles in degrees by use of a multiplication factor. Since one radian is equal to $\dfrac{180}{\pi} = 57.3°$ approximately, the angle in radians must be multiplied by 57.3. For convenience, a mark designated r has been placed at this point on the C and D scales on one face of the rule. For example, to convert 1.71 radians to degrees, set the left index of C at 1.71 on D; move the hairline to r on C; read 98° on D at the hairline. To convert 14.9° to radians, set the hairline at 14.9 on D; move r on C to hairline; read 0.260 radians on D at the right index of C.

**Operations Involving Very Small Angles.** It will be remembered that for very small angles the sine function, tangent function, and the angle in radians are very nearly equal. Thus within the limits of slide rule accuracy these three functions for very small angles may be used interchangeably. Since angles are quite often expressed in degrees, minutes, and seconds, a special mark (a single dot) is provided on the ST scale for the conversion of minutes to radians. One minute is equal to $\frac{\pi}{180(60)}$ radians which is approximately $\frac{1}{3437}$ radians. The conversion mark therefore appears on the ST scale approximately at 3440 on the C scale. Its use may be illustrated by the following example: to determine the angle in radians or the sine or tangent function of $0° - 49.2'$, set the hairline at 49.2 on D; move the minute mark on ST to the hairline; read 0.0143 on D at the left index of C. Hence 0.0143 is the angle in radians or we may say that the sine or the tangent of $0° - 49.2'$ is equal to 0.0143.

An additional mark is provided on the ST scale for the conversion of angles in seconds to radians, or for obtaining the sine or tangent of such angles. This consists of a double dot. One second is equal to $\frac{\pi}{180(60)60} = \frac{1}{206,240}$ radians, approximately. Thus the conversion mark for seconds appears opposite approximately 206,000 on the C scale. It is of use in operations such as determining the sine or tangent of $0° - 0' - 29''$. Setting the hairline at 29 on D, we move the seconds mark on ST to the hairline, reading 0.0001406 on D at the left index of C.

# Chapter 7

## APPLICATIONS TO CIVIL ENGINEERING

### by E. I. FIESENHEISER, B.S., M.S., C.E.

**Purpose.** The purpose of this chapter is to illustrate some of the many applications of the slide rule to civil engineering problems. (Other chapters illustrating other fields of engineering follow.) No attempt is made to cover the entire field of civil engineering since to do so would require many volumes. Only a few typical problems from various branches of this field are discussed. Equations, where used, are given without derivation.

**Accuracy.** The slide rule is always useful for checking even though its accuracy is not always sufficient for a particular problem solution. In calculating dimensions and long lengths with precision it is often necessary to resort to the use of five or seven place logarithms, or to extensive tables of natural functions for use with a mechanical calculator. This is particularly true in surveying problems. In such cases errors may sometimes be discovered by approximate slide rule checking of a precisely calculated result. In the field of stress analysis or design the accuracy of the slide rule is ordinarily sufficient.

## SURVEYING PROBLEMS

**Earthwork Quantities.** The slide rule is useful in calculating the amount of earthwork to be moved for the construction of a highway. The contour of the ground is determined by leveling along the proposed line of the road and the area of the cross sections perpendicular to this line are calculated at various stations along the road. V, the volume of earth to be moved, may then be determined by either of two methods. The first method is called the "average end area" method in which $V = \frac{1}{2}(A_1 + A_2)L$, where $A_1$ and $A_2$ are cross sectional areas and L is the distance between them. For example: $A_1$ is calculated as 162 (ft.)$^2$ and $A_2$ as 184 (ft.)$^2$, with the distance L between the sections 54 ft. $V = \frac{1}{2}(162 + 184)54 = 173(54) = 9,340(ft.)^3$ by slide rule.

While the above method is simple, it is not exact. When greater precision is desired the "prismoidal" formula is used. This method involves an additional area $A_m$, the area of a cross section half-way between $A_1$ and $A_2$. By the prismiodal formula $V = \frac{1}{6}(A_1 + 4A_m + A_2)L$. For example, for $A_1 = 500(\text{ft.})^2$, $A_m = 684(\text{ft.})^2$, $A_2 = 896(\text{ft.})^2$, and $L = 92$ ft.: $V = \frac{1}{6}(500 + 2736 + 896)92 = \frac{1}{6}(3,312)92 = 48,000(\text{ft.})^3$ by slide rule.

**Exercise 146.** Calculate the volume of earthwork to be moved between two stations 73.4 ft. apart if $A_1 = 124$ $(\text{ft.})^2$, $A_m = 136$ $(\text{ft.})^2$, and $A_2 = 154$ $(\text{ft.})^2$. (a) By the average end area method; (b) by the "prismoidal" formula.

**Taping.** When measuring distances by tape in the field, many times it is necessary to measure along a slope in hilly country, although the horizontal distance is desired. It is then necessary to correct the slope measurement. This may be done if the angle of slope is determined by use of a transit. If S is the slope measurement or taped distance, h the horizontal length and A the angle of slope, then $h = S \cdot \cos A$. For example if $S = 100$ ft. and $A = 15°$: $h = 100 \cos 15° = 96.6$ ft. by slide rule.

A common source of error is the use of a tape too long or too short. However, if the tape being used is compared with a standard and the error in its length determined, a correction may be made. For example, in measuring a line by use of a 100 ft. tape the measured distance was 864.91 ft. The tape was found to be 0.14 ft. too long. The correction is $\frac{864.91}{100}(0.14) = 1.21$ ft. by slide rule. This error of 1.21 ft. must be added to 864.91 ft. to give the correct length as 866.12 ft. (Had the tape been 0.14 ft. too short, the correction would have been subtracted.)

**Exercise 147.** A distance measured by a 50 ft. steel tape was found to be 484.15 ft. If the tape used was actually 0.028 ft. too short, what is the true length of the line?

**Latitudes and Departures.** In locating a point with reference to a previously located point from field survey data, the method of latitudes and departures is often used. The latitude is defined as the component of a given distance in the north-south direction whereas the departure is the component in the east-west direction. The bearing of a line is the angle between the line and the true north.

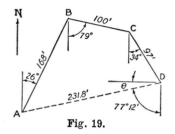

**Fig. 19.**

| Line | Dist. | Bearing | LAT. | | DEP. | |
| --- | --- | --- | --- | --- | --- | --- |
| | | | N. | S. | E. | W. |
| AB | 168 | N. 26° E. | 151.0 | | 73.6′ | |
| BC | 100 | S. 79° E. | | 19.1′ | 98.1′ | |
| CD | 97 | S. 34° E. | | 80.5′ | 54.3′ | |
| DA | | | | 51.4′ N. | | 226.0′ E. |

Fig. 19 represents a plot of a field traverse made by taping distances AB, BC, and CD. At each point a bearing was taken. These and the taped distances are recorded in the table. The line AD was not measured in the field. Nevertheless its length and bearing are desired.

It may be seen from the figure that the latitude of each distance is the length multiplied by the cosine of the bearing angle and the departure is the length multiplied by the sine of the bearing. The necessary multiplications, performed by slide rule, are set down in the appropriate columns of the table. After summing the distances we observe that point D is 51.4′ north and 226.0′ east of A. Length DA is therefore $\sqrt{(51.4)^2 + (226.0)^2} = 231.8'$. Angle $\theta$ in the figure is then arc sin $\frac{51.4}{231.8} = 12.8°$ or $12°-48'$. The same angle may be determined from the relationship $\theta = $ arc tan $\frac{51.4}{226}$ which also yields 12.8°. The bearing of point A from point D is then $90° - \theta$ and since A is south and west of D, the bearing is designated S. $77° - 12'$ W. The same calculations, performed with 5-place logarithmic tables, result in a bearing of S. $77° - 09' - 54''$ W. and a length DA = 231.84′. Line DA represents the closing line of the traverse. It is obvious that the slide rule calculations provide an accurate check.

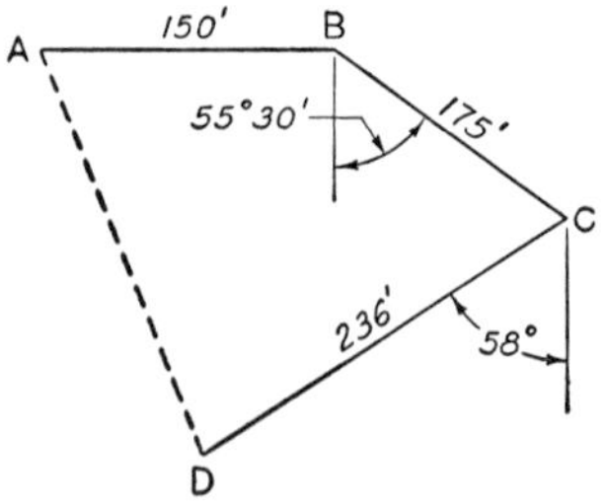

**Exercise 148.** Solve for the length of the closing line DA in the traverse shown in Fig. 20. Calculate its bearing.

**Fig. 20.**

**Inaccessible Distances.** In running a survey line obstacles may occur on the line of sight or it may be impossible to measure certain lengths such as the distance across a river. In such cases it is necessary to extend the line by indirect methods. Fig. 21 illustrates a method for passing an obstacle by use of angular deflections. Point B is a point

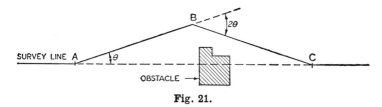

Fig. 21.

visible from A. The procedure then is to measure distance AB and the angle $\Theta$. The angle at B is then taken as 2 $\Theta$ and the length BC as equal to AB. By sighting along BC point C may be located. Distance AC is then $2(AB) \cos \Theta$. For example if AB measures 94' and $\Theta = 21.8°$, then AC $= 2(94') \cos 21.8° = 174.6'$.

**Exercise 149.** If, in passing an obstacle, the deflection angle measured by transit at A was 37° and the taped distance AB was 86 ft., determine the length AC.

Fig. 22 illustrates a method for extending a survey line across a river when it is not practical to measure directly across. Point C is visible from either A or B.

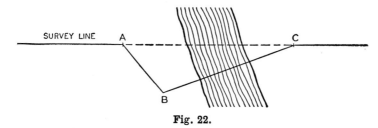

Fig. 22.

Angles at A and B are measured by the use of a transit and distance AB is accurately measured by tape. The angle at C will then be $180° - A - B$. Then by the law of sines $\dfrac{AC}{AB} = \dfrac{\sin B}{\sin C}$. For example if $A = 73° - 18'$, $B = 101°$, and AB $= 54'$, then $C = 180° - 73.3° - 101° = 5.7°$. $\dfrac{AC}{54'} = \dfrac{\sin 101°}{\sin 5.7°} = \dfrac{\cos 11°}{\sin 5.7°}$, from which AC $= 534'$ by slide rule, using the proportion principle previously explained. A calculation using 5-place logarithmic tables yields AC = 533.7′.

**Exercise 150.** Referring to Fig. 22, determine the distance AC across a river if AB = 75 ft. and angles at A and B are 47° and 115° respectively.

**Stadia Calculations.** A stadia transit is an instrument for determining horizontal and vertical distances from the observer to a point by taking readings on a rod held vertically at the point. By this method it is unnecessary to tape the distance from the observer to the point. The transit telescope is provided with an upper, lower, and a middle horizontal cross hair. The upper and lower cross hairs are equidistant from the middle cross hair which represents the line of sight of the telescope. A special stadia rod is held at the point to be located and the transit is focused on this rod. Rod readings are taken at the upper and lower cross hairs and the rod length between these points, called the rod intercept r, is determined. Also the vertical angle Θ, between the line of sight and the horizontal, is read at the transit.

The horizontal distance H from the observer to the point is then calculated by the equation $H = a \cos \Theta + kr \cos^2\Theta$, in which a and k are instrumental constants, known for any particular transit. The vertical distance from the telescope to the middle cross hair is $V = a \sin\Theta + \frac{1}{2}kr \sin 2\Theta$. For example, suppose the upper and lower cross hair readings to be 4.32′ and 1.14′ respectively, with a vertical angle $\Theta = 26°$. The rod intercept r = 4.32′ − 1.14′ = 3.18′. Assume instrumental constants a and k to be 1′ and 100 respectively. Then $H = 1 \cdot \cos 26° + 100(3.18) \cos^2 26° = 0.9′ + 257 = 258′$ approx. $V = 1 \cdot \sin 26° + \frac{1}{2}(100)$. 3.18 sin 52° = 0.4′ + 125.1 = 125.5′. This is the difference in elevation between the transit telescope and the center of the rod intercept. Ordinarily stadia distance calculations are made only to the nearest foot, for which the slide rule provides ample accuracy.

**Exercise 151.** If the instrumental constants a and k are 1′ and 100 respectively, determine the vertical and horizontal distances V and H from the following stadia readings:

|     | Vertical Angle Θ | Rod Intercept |
| --- | --- | --- |
| (a) | 10°−15′ | 5.42 ft. |
| (b) | 7°−30′ | 2.14 ft. |
| (c) | 19°−45′ | 4.25 ft. |

**Radius and Degree of Curve of a Curved Track.** In railroad track surveying it is possible to calculate the radius and the degree of curve from measured lengths of a straight chord C and the mid-ordinate M.

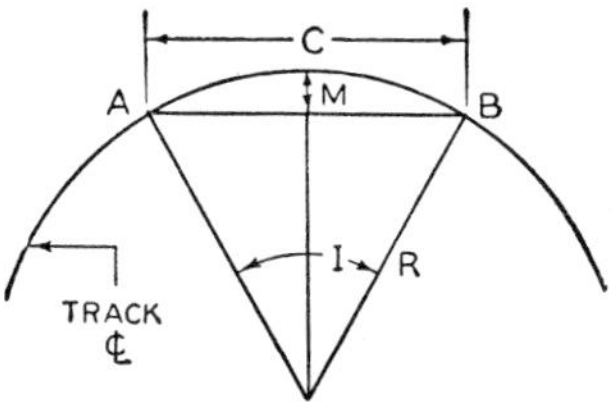

**Fig. 23.**

$$R = \frac{C^2 + 4M^2}{8M}.$$

$$D = \frac{5730'}{R} \text{ (approx.) and}$$

$$D = 2 \text{ arc sin } \frac{50}{R} \text{ (exact)}.$$

$$I = 2 \text{ arc sin } \frac{C}{2R}.$$

In Fig. 23 formulas for calculating the radius R and degree of curve D are given. The degree of curve is the central angle subtended by a 100' chord. As an example, suppose the distance C to be 300' and at 150' from A the ordinate M is found to be 2.15'. The radius is then $\frac{90,000 + 18.5}{17.2} =$ 5230' approx. and the degree of curve is $D = \frac{5730'}{5230'} = 1.095° = 1° -$ 5.7'. The central angle $I = 2 \text{ arc sin } \frac{300}{10,460} = 2(1.644°) = 3.288°$.

**Exercise 152.** Determine the radius R, degree of curve D, and central angle I for the following values of the chord C and the mid-ordinate M:

|     | C | M |
| --- | --- | --- |
| (a) | 208 ft. | 6.4 ft. |
| (b) | 147 ft. | 5.65 ft. |
| (c) | 61.5 ft. | 1.27 ft. |

## STRUCTURAL DRAFTING

**Lengths and Bevels.** The structural steel draftsman is concerned mainly with the calculation of the lengths of members and the details of their connections to other members in the structure. These lengths and details are shown on drawings which are used in the shop for fabrication of the various members. Many times it is necessary for members to be skewed and to connect to other members at an angle. The skew of a connection is ordinarily indicated on the drawing by a bevel which is a figure calculated to the nearest $\frac{1}{16}$ of an inch for the distance perpendicular to a base line 12″ long. Thus in Fig. 24 the distance R is known as the bevel.

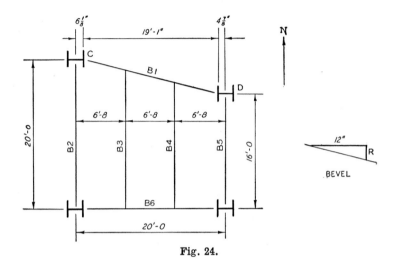

**Fig. 24.**

Fig. 24 represents a floor plan in which columns and beams are shown. The beams are indicated by heavy lines and are marked B1 to B6 inclusive. Due to the skew of beam B1 it will be necessary to calculate the lengths of B1, B3, and B4 and the bevel due to the skew. Beam B1 will be connected at the mid point of the flanges of columns C and D. All distances must be figured to the nearest $\frac{1}{16}$″.

The bevel can be calculated or checked by slide rule, using the principle of proportion. Column D is $4'-0$ south of column C and its flange face is $19'-1''$ or 229″ east of that of column C. The bevel R is found as follows:

$$\frac{R}{12''} = \frac{4'-0}{19'-1} = \frac{48''}{229''}$$
$$R = 2\tfrac{1}{2}''$$

The length of B1 will be $\sqrt{(229)^2 + (48)^2} = \sqrt{52,500 + 2,300} = \sqrt{54,800} = 234'' = 19'-6''$. The R1 and R2 scales were used for determining the squares and the square root of their sum.

The length of B4 will be greater than $16' - 0$. The increase in length will be termed D' and will be determined by the proportion $\dfrac{D'}{6' - 3\frac{1}{8}''} = \dfrac{48''}{229''}$ or $\dfrac{D'}{75.1''} = \dfrac{48''}{229''}$ from which $D' = 15.73''$ or $1' - 3\frac{3}{4}''$ by proportion. Then the length of B4 will be $16' - 0 + 1' - 3\frac{3}{4}'' = 17' - 3\frac{3}{4}''$.

The proportion for determining the increased length of B3 will be $\dfrac{D'}{12' - 11\frac{1}{8}''} = \dfrac{48''}{229''}$ or $\dfrac{D'}{155.1''} = \dfrac{48''}{229''}$, from which $D' = 32.5''$ or $2' - 8\frac{1}{2}''$. Hence the length of B3 is $16' - 0 + 2' - 8\frac{1}{2}'' = 18' - 8\frac{1}{2}''$.

**Exercise 153.** Determine the lengths C and bevels R for values A and B given below:

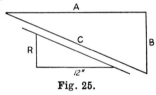

| | A | B |
|---|---|---|
| (a) | $4' - 5\frac{1}{4}$ | $2' - 8$ |
| (b) | $8' - 7\frac{3}{4}$ | $7' - 7$ |
| (c) | $14' - 9$ | $4' - 9\frac{5}{8}$ |

Fig. 25.

**The Miter Joint.** A miter joint is one in which intersecting members meet on a common line of contact. In detailing the top chord members of a bridge truss, and in other cases, it is important to know the angle or bevel of the line of intersection. Fig. 26 indicates the manner in which this angle, designated $\phi$, may be determined. The depths $d_1$ and $d_2$ and angles of slope $\Theta_1$ and $\Theta_2$ are known for the intersecting members. The

$$\text{Tan } \phi = \frac{d_1 \cos \Theta_2 - d_2 \cos \Theta_1}{d_2 \sin \Theta_1 - d_1 \sin \Theta_2}$$

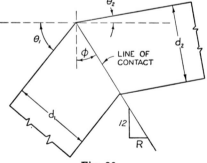

Fig. 26.

tangent of angle $\phi$ may be determined from the formula. As an example: $d_1 = 12\frac{3}{4}''$, $d_2 = 12\frac{1}{2}''$, $\Theta_1 = 48°$ and $\Theta_2 = 9° - 30' - 45''$ or $9.51°$. Then

$$\tan \phi = \frac{12.75 \cos 9.51° - 12.5 \cos 48°}{12.5 \sin 48° - 12.75 \sin 9.51°} = \frac{12.58 - 8.36}{9.28 - 2.10} = \frac{4.22}{7.18} = 0.588.$$

$\phi$ = arc tan 0.588 = 30.4°.

The bevel R = 12 tan $\phi$ = 7.06″ or 7$\frac{1}{16}$″. This bevel, calculated by slide rule, was also calculated by 5-place logarithmic tables. Both methods give the same result to the nearest $\frac{1}{16}$″.

**Exercise 154.** Determine the bevel R for miter joints having the following properties:

|     | $\theta_1$ | $\theta_2$ | $d_1$ | $d_2$ |
|-----|-----|-----|-----|-----|
| (a) | 40° | 11° | 14″ | 12″ |
| (b) | 49° | 8° | 11$\frac{1}{2}$″ | 9$\frac{1}{2}$″ |
| (c) | 52° | 0° | 7$\frac{1}{2}$″ | 7$\frac{1}{2}$″ |

## STRUCTURAL ANALYSIS

**The Truss.** In the stress analysis of structural members it is necessary to work constantly with the applied forces. A force, being a vector quantity having both magnitude and direction, may be resolved into components (as in Chapter 6). If convenient, the components may be used separately. As an example, Fig. 24 (a) shows a force of 250# acting on a two member truss. The forces in members A and B are to be deter-

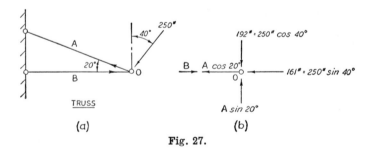

**Fig. 27.**

mined. For convenience the force A and the applied 250# force are resolved into their horizontal and vertical components. Force B is horizontal and has no vertical component. All forces and components acting at point 0 are shown in Fig. 24 (b).

To maintain equilibrium the sum of vertical forces must be zero and the sum of horizontal forces must also be zero. Hence from Fig. 27 (b), $192 - A \sin 20° = 0$, from which $A = \dfrac{192}{\sin 20°} = 562\#$. Also $B - A \cos 20° - 161 = 0$, from which $B = 161 + 562 \cos 20° = 161 + 527 = 688\#$. All of the operations are performed using the Cos S scales.

**Exercise 155.** Calculate the stresses in the members of trusses shown below in figures 28 (a) and (b). Indicate whether the stresses calculated represent tension or compression.

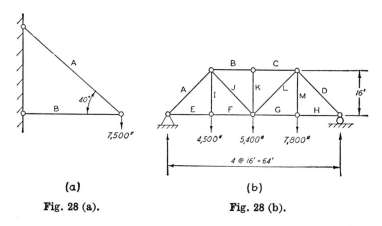

(a)

**Fig. 28 (a).**

(b)

**Fig. 28 (b).**

**A Steel Beam.** In determining the stresses in a beam it is necessary to determine the forces acting, the shear, and the bending moment. The internal stresses in the material are then determined from the theory of the strength of materials. As an example, Fig. 29 illustrates a steel beam designed to carry a concentrated load of 8,800# on a span of 11'.

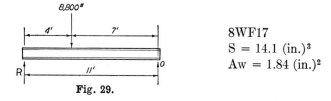

**Fig. 29.**

8WF17
$S = 14.1$ (in.)$^3$
$Aw = 1.84$ (in.)$^2$

Its section modulus S and web area Aw are given for use in determining the moment and shear stresses in the material.

The left reaction force R may be determined by proportion, utilizing the distances from point 0 at the right end of the span. $\dfrac{R}{8,800} = \dfrac{7'}{11'}$, from which R = 5,600#. This force is the shear acting at the left of the load. It will be resisted primarily by the web area. Hence the shearing unit stress $\dfrac{5,600}{1.84} = 3,050\#$ per sq. in.

The moment under the 8,800# load will be the product R × 4' = 5,600(4) = 22,400'#. The unit stress due to this bending moment will be $\dfrac{22,400(12)}{14.1} = 19,000\#$ per sq. in.

Stress analysis problems having to do with steel beams are many and varied. The above example is intended to serve merely as an illustration of this type of calculation to which the slide rule is well adapted.

**Exercise 156.** Solve for the end reactions $R_L$ and $R_R$ and for the moment in the beam at each load point. Calculate the maximum bending stress for the loads shown if the section modulus of the beam is 107.8 (in.)³.

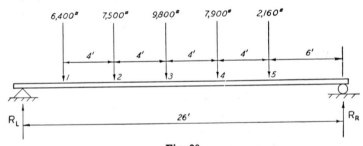

Fig. 30.

**A Reinforced Concrete Beam.** For a simple concrete beam, reinforced by steel to resist tension, it is necessary to determine the location of the neutral axis of the cross section before the bending moment stresses can be determined. The strength of the concrete in tension is ignored. In Fig. 31 the cross section of a beam is shown, for which the concrete compressive unit stress $f_c$ and unit stress in the steel $f_s$ are to be determined when the moment is 440,000"#.

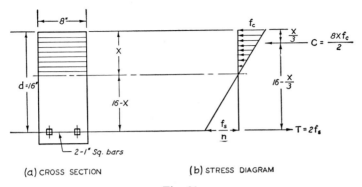

(a) CROSS SECTION    (b) STRESS DIAGRAM

Fig. 31.

The effective area of steel is equivalent to n times its actual area, where n is the modular ratio, assumed equal to 10 in this case. The effective steel area is therefore $2 \times 10 = 20$ sq. in. The neutral axis may be located by equating the moments of effective tensile and compressive areas about this line. Thus $8X\left(\dfrac{X}{2}\right) = 20(16 - X)$ or $X^2 + 5X - 80 = 0$. This is a quadratic equation which may be solved for X by the factoring method previously described in Chapter 3. Setting the right index of the C scale at 80 on D, the hairline is moved to 6.78 on CI where the simultaneous hairline reading on D is 11.78, the difference of these two readings being 5. The neutral axis is therefore located at $X = 6.78''$. The lever arm between the forces C and T is $16 - \dfrac{X}{3} = 13.74''$, and the moment is either C or T times this lever arm. Hence $\dfrac{8(6.78)}{2} \cdot f_c \cdot (13.74) = 440,000$ and $f_c = 1,180\#$ per sq. in. From the equation $2f_s(13.74) = 440,000$, $f_s = 16,000\#$ per sq. in.

**Exercise 157.** A concrete beam $12\frac{1}{2}$ in. wide, with an effective depth d of 27 in., is reinforced by four 1-inch dia. rods. If the value of n is 10, locate the neutral axis and determine $f_c$ and $f_s$ for a bending moment of 1,500,000 in. lb.

**A Filled Arch.** Arches are frequently used to carry loads over long spans. They are economical structures provided the end supports are capable of withstanding the thrusts transmitted by the arch rib and provided the curve of the arch axis is properly designed. A well designed

arch curve will be such that the applied loads produce primarily forces
or thrusts, with little or no bending moment.

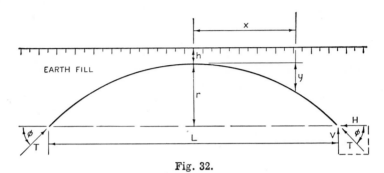

Fig. 32.

In Fig. 32 the primary load to be carried consists of an earth fill. The
weight of this fill is termed w lb. per cubic foot. In order to carry this
load without introducing bending moment the arch axis curve must be
determined by the equation $y = h\left(\cosh\sqrt{\dfrac{w}{H}}(x) - 1\right)$, where H is the
horizontal component of the thrust to be resisted by a section of arch
rib one foot in width. If the ratio of depths of fill is $g = \dfrac{h + r}{h}$, then

$$H = \frac{wL^2}{4[\text{Log}_e(g + \sqrt{g^2 - 1})]^2}.$$

The angle of slope $\phi$, at the end of the arch, may be determined from
the expression $\tan\phi = h\sqrt{\dfrac{w}{H}}\cdot\sinh\left(\dfrac{L}{2}\sqrt{\dfrac{w}{H}}\right)$. Then the vertical component of thrust $V = H.\tan\phi$ and the maximum thrust $T = \dfrac{H}{\cos\phi}$.

As an example for slide rule computation the following data will be
used: $L = 200'$, $w = 120$ lb. per cu. ft., $r = 40'$ and $h = 10'$. g is then

$$= \frac{10 + 40}{10} = 5 \text{ and } H = \frac{120(200)^2}{4 \cdot [\text{Log}_e (5 + \sqrt{24})]^2} = \frac{1,200,000}{(\text{Log}_e 9.9)^2} =$$

$$\frac{1,200,000}{(2.294)^2} = 228,000 \text{ lb.}$$

$$\text{Tan } \phi = 10\sqrt{\frac{120}{228,000}} \cdot \sinh\left(\frac{200}{2}\sqrt{\frac{120}{228,000}}\right) = 0.2294 \sinh (2.294).$$

Since sinh $(2.294) = \frac{1}{2}(e^{2.294} - e^{-2.294})$, tan $\phi = 0.2294 \cdot \frac{1}{2}(9.900 - 0.101) = 1.124$, from which the angle $\phi = 48.4°$.

$$V = H \tan \phi = 256,500 \text{ lb. and } T = \frac{H}{\cos \phi} = 343,000 \text{ lb.}$$

The equation locating the arch axis will be $y = 10\left(\cosh \frac{x}{43.6} - 1\right)$. By substituting values of x equal to any horizontal distance from the center line, the corresponding ordinate y may be determined. For example, at the quarter point of the span, $x = 50'$. At this point $y = 10\left(\cosh \frac{50}{43.6} - 1\right) = 10[\frac{1}{2}(e^{1.147} + e^{-1.147}) - 1] = 10[\frac{1}{2}(3.145 + 0.318) - 1] = 10(1.731 - 1) = 7.31'$.

For structures of this type the log log scales are very useful in evaluating logarithms and hyperbolic functions.

**Exercise 158.** Determine the economical curve equation for a 300 ft.-span filled arch if the depth of fill h is 6 ft. at the center and the rise r is 50 ft. If the fill weighs 120#/cu. ft. determine the forces H, V, and T for a one-foot width of arch rib.

**A Gravity Dam.** Gravity dams are structures in which the weight of the dam itself is utilized to balance the pressure of water and to prevent overturning. In calculating the pressures on the base and in investigating the stability of such structures, the weight of each part of the dam is calculated separately. Then the moment of all forces about a common point is determined and the resultant force acting on the base of the dam is located.

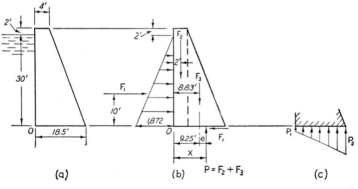

Fig. 33.

In Fig. 33 (a) a simple dam is shown which is to retain a 30′ head of water weighing 62.4 lb. per cu. ft. For analysis a width of dam of one foot, perpendicular to the figure, is used. The dam is to be constructed of concrete assumed to weigh 145 lb. per cu. ft. Fig. 33 (b) indicates the separate forces and their locations. Distance x, locating the resultant vertical component P, is to be determined.

The water pressure acts horizontally and at the bottom of the dam has an intensity of 62.4(30′) = 1,872 lb. per foot. The total force due to water pressure is the area of the force triangle and is termed $F_1$. $F_1 = \dfrac{30}{2}(1,872) = 28,100$ lb. The forces $F_2$ and $F_3$ are due to the weight of concrete, $F_2$ being equal to 145(4)32 = 18,600 lb. and $F_3$ being $\dfrac{145(14.5)32}{2} = 33,600$ lb. The moment of forces $F_1$, $F_2$, and $F_3$ about point 0 is balanced by the moment P·x, shown in Fig. 33 (b). Therefore (18,600 + 33,600) x = 28,100(10) + 18,600(2) + 33,600(8.83).

$$x = \frac{615,000}{52,200} = 11.78'.$$

The eccentricity e, measured from the center line of the base, is then 11.78′ − 9.25′ = 2.53′. Pressures $p_1$ and $p_2$ indicated in Fig. 33 (c) may now be determined from the equations $p_1 = \dfrac{P}{L}\left(1 - \dfrac{6e}{L}\right)$ $\dfrac{52,200}{18.5}\left(1 - \dfrac{6(2.53)}{18.5}\right) = 2,820(1 - 0.821) = 506$ lb. per sq. ft.; and $p_2 = \dfrac{P}{L}\left(1 + \dfrac{6e}{L}\right) = 2,820(1 + 0.821) = 5,140$ lb. per sq. ft. The resultant is located within the base, since x < 18.5′, which indicates that the dam is stable and will not overturn.

**Exercise 159.** Determine the base pressures $p_1$ and $p_2$ for a dam 30 ft. high if the width is 3 ft. at the top and 14 ft. at the bottom. The depth of water retained is to be 24 ft. and the weight of masonry is 145#/cu. ft.

# Chapter 8

## APPLICATIONS TO MECHANICAL ENGINEERING

### *by* R. A. BUDENHOLZER, B.S., M.S., Ph.D.

### INTRODUCTION

The subject of mechanical engineering is so diversified that it would be quite impossible to cover even a small portion of the many types of problems which may readily be solved with the aid of the slide rule. Although many of these problems are simple and require only the use of the basic scales designed for multiplication and division, there are others which require considerable skill in the use of the more complicated scales. It is the purpose of this chapter to acquaint the student with some of the latter and to illustrate their solution with the Post Versalog Slide Rule.

There are several fields of mechanical engineering in which an abundance of problems exist whose solutions are particularly suited to the slide rule. Of these, perhaps the most important are thermodynamics, heat transfer, and machine design. In this chapter, each of these branches will be treated separately, and a few representative examples, together with their solutions, will be included. The treatment assumes that the student already possesses a basic knowledge of the use of all scales, and that he is familiar with the technique of setting decimal points and of performing other commonly employed operations. In studying the illustrative examples, the student is urged to follow the operations listed, and at each step to call to mind the reason why the particular operation was employed, and why it accomplishes its objective. In this way, a more basic understanding of the rule will gradually be achieved, leading soon to a complete mastery of its operation.

### THERMODYNAMICS

The science of thermodynamics is related to the behavior of gases, liquids, and solids when under the influence of the interchange of heat and mechanical energy. A large number of problems in which the use of the log-log scales are particularly valuable are those involving the behavior of perfect gases undergoing changes in state. The derivation

# TABLE I

Thermodynamic Equations For Perfect Gases (Non-Flow Processes)

| Name of Process | Value of n | P-V-T Relationships | | | Heat Added $_1Q_2$ Btu | Work Done By Gas $_1W_2$ Btu | Change In Internal Energy $U_2-U_1$ Btu | Change In Enthalpy $H_2-H_1$ Btu | Change In Entropy $S_2-S_1$ Btu/°R |
|---|---|---|---|---|---|---|---|---|---|
| | | P-V | T-P | T-V | | | | | |
| Constant Volume $V$=Const. | $\infty$ | — | $\dfrac{T_1}{T_2}=\dfrac{P_1}{P_2}$ | — | $wc_v(T_2-T_1)$ | $0$ | $wc_v(T_2-T_1)$ | $wc_p(T_2-T_1)$ | $wc_v\log_e\dfrac{T_2}{T_1}$ |
| Constant Pressure $P$=Const. | $0$ | — | — | $\dfrac{T_1}{T_2}=\dfrac{V_1}{V_2}$ | $wc_p(T_2-T_1)$ | $\dfrac{P(V_2-V_1)}{J}$ | $wc_v(T_2-T_1)$ | $wc_p(T_2-T_1)$ | $wc_p\log_e\dfrac{T_2}{T_1}$ |
| Isothermal $T$=Const. | $1$ | $\dfrac{P_1}{P_2}=\dfrac{V_2}{V_1}$ | — | — | $\dfrac{wRT}{J}\log_e\dfrac{P_1}{P_2}$ | $\dfrac{wRT}{J}\log_e\dfrac{P_1}{P_2}$ | $0$ | $0$ | $\dfrac{wR}{J}\log_e\dfrac{P_2}{P_1}$ |
| Isentropic $S$=Const. | $k$ | $\dfrac{P_1}{P_2}=\left(\dfrac{V_2}{V_1}\right)^{k}$ | $\dfrac{T_1}{T_2}=\left(\dfrac{P_1}{P_2}\right)^{\frac{k-1}{k}}$ | $\dfrac{T_1}{T_2}=\left(\dfrac{V_2}{V_1}\right)^{k-1}$ | $0$ | $wc_v(T_2-T_1)$ | $wc_v(T_2-T_1)$ | $wc_p(T_2-T_1)$ | $0$ |
| Polytropic $PV^n$=Const. | $n$ | $\dfrac{P_1}{P_2}=\left(\dfrac{V_2}{V_1}\right)^{n}$ | $\dfrac{T_1}{T_2}=\left(\dfrac{P_1}{P_2}\right)^{\frac{n-1}{n}}$ | $\dfrac{T_1}{T_2}=\left(\dfrac{V_2}{V_1}\right)^{n-1}$ | $wc_n(T_2-T_1)$ | $\dfrac{wR}{J(n-1)}(T_1-T_2)$ | $wc_v(T_2-T_1)$ | $wc_p(T_2-T_1)$ | $wc_n\log_e\dfrac{T_2}{T_1}$ |

$c_v$ = Specific heat at constant volume, Btu/lb.
$c_p$ = Specific heat at constant pressure, Btu/lb.
$c_n$ = Specific heat for a polytropic process = $c_v\left(\dfrac{k-n}{1-n}\right)$, Btu/lb.

$H$ = Enthalpy, Btu.
$J$ = Mechanical Equivalent of heat, 778 Ft. lbs./Btu.
$k$ = Isentropic exponent, $c_p/c_v$.
$n$ = Polytropic exponent.

$P$ = pressure, lbs./ft.²
$R$ = Gas constant, ft./°R.
$R$ = Gas constant, ft./°R.
$S$ = Entropy, Btu./°R.
$T$ = Absolute temperature, °R = (460 + F)
$U$ = Internal Energy, Btu.
$V$ = Volume, ft.³
$w$ = Weight of gas, lbs.

of the equations expressing the various relationships existing between such properties as pressure, absolute temperature, volume, internal energy, enthalpy, and entropy can be found in any standard textbook on thermodynamics. These equations are usually derived for certain commonly employed processes such as constant volume, constant pressure, isothermal, isentropic, and polytropic. In table I are presented those equations which have been found to be most useful to the mechanical engineer. The nomenclature employed is expressed in engineering units.

A study of Table I shows that all equations listed fall into one or more of the following three categories: equations involving powers of numbers; equations involving the natural logarithms of numbers; equations involving simple multiplication or division.

Of these, only the first two are sufficiently difficult to require special treatment in this chapter.

## a. Equations Involving Powers of Numbers

Solution of these equations is accomplished by the use of the log-log scales, LL3 to LL0 and LL/3 to LL/0. In many cases, several alternative solutions of equal accuracy and speed will suggest themselves. At first, the student should employ more than one method, using the other as a check. After proficiency in all methods is achieved, the student should be able to select for himself the one best suited to the particular circumstances.

### Example 1.

For a polytropic process, solve for $P_2$ if $n = 1.21$, $P_1 = 120$ psia, and $V_2 = 3.17V_1$. Answer 29.7 psia.

### Solution:

From Table I write, $\quad P_2 = \dfrac{P_1}{\left(\dfrac{V_2}{V_1}\right)^n} = \dfrac{120}{3.17^{1.21}}$

Set left index of C opposite 3.17 on LL3. Move hairline to 1.21 on C and read 4.04 on LL3. Set 4.04 on C opposite 120 on D and read 29.7 opposite right index of C.

### Alternate Solution:

Write, $\quad P_2 = P_1\left(\dfrac{V_1}{V_2}\right)^n = 120\left(\dfrac{1}{3.17}\right)^{1.21} = 120 \times 0.315^{1.21}$

Set hairline over 3.17 on LL3 and read its reciprocal 0.315 on LL/3. Slide left index of C under hairline and move hairline to 1.21 on C. Read 0.247 on LL/3. This is $0.315^{1.21}$. Set left index of C to 120 on D and move hairline to 0.247 on C. Read 29.7 on D.

**Example 2.**

For a polytropic process, find n if $\dfrac{P_1}{P_2} = 7.23$ and $\dfrac{V_2}{V_1} = 5.63$.

Answer 1.145

**Solution:**

From Table I write, $\dfrac{P_1}{P_2} = \left(\dfrac{V_2}{V_1}\right)^n$ or $7.23 = 5.63^n$

Set left index of C opposite 5.63 on LL3. Move hairline to 7.23 on LL3 and read n = 1.145 on C.

**Alternate Solution:**

An alternate, but much less rapid solution, may be obtained by using natural logarithms. Write

$$\log_e 7.23 = n \log_e 5.63$$

or

$$n = \frac{\log_e 7.23}{\log_e 5.63}$$

Find $\log_e 5.63$ by setting hairline to 5.63 on LL3 and reading 1.73 on D. Find $\log_e 7.23$ by setting hairline to 7.23 on LL3 and reading 1.98 on D. Slide 1.73 on C under hairline and read 1.145 on D opposite left index of C.

The same result could have been obtained using common logarithms and reading their values on the L scale. Thus

$$n = \frac{\log_{10} 7.23}{\log_{10} 5.63} = \frac{0.859}{0.75} = 1.145$$

**Example 3.**

For a polytropic process find $\dfrac{V_2}{V_1}$ if $\dfrac{T_2}{T_1} = 0.94$ and n = 1.037.

Answer 5.30

**Solution:**

$$\frac{T_1}{T_2} = \left(\frac{V_2}{V_1}\right)^{n-1} \quad \text{Therefore} \quad \frac{1}{0.94} = \left(\frac{V_2}{V_1}\right)^{0.037}$$

The simplest solution is to find the number which, when raised to the 0.037 power will give $\frac{1}{0.94}$. Set hair line to 0.94 on LL/1 and read its reciprocal 1.0637 on LL1. Slide 0.037 on C under the hairline and read 5.30 opposite left index of C on LL3. The choice of the correct LL scale on which to read the answer is governed by the position of the decimal point. In this case, since the decimal point is in the second place to the left of 3.7, it is necessary to move upward two scales to the LL3, in order to obtain the correct result.

## Alternate Solution (Preferred):

$$\frac{V_2}{V_1} = \left(\frac{1}{0.94}\right)^{\frac{1}{0.037}} = \left(\frac{1}{0.94}\right)^{27}$$

Opposite 0.94 on LL/1 set right index of C. Move hairline to 27 on C and read 5.30 on LL3. The first operation above was equivalent to setting the right index of C opposite 1.0637 (the reciprocal of 0.94) on D. The second operation raised 1.0637 to the 27 power. Again, the choice of LL scale on which the answer is read is determined by the position of the decimal point. In this case, it is clear that the answer would not be on the LL2 scale because this would give 1.1815, which would be the answer had the exponent been 2.7 instead of 27.

## Example 4.

Solve example 3 if n = 1.37. Answer 1.1815

## Solution:

The solution in this case is identical with that of example 3 except that the exponent by the first method becomes 0.37 instead of 0.037. By the second method it becomes 2.7 instead of 27. The answer is 1.1815 instead of 5.30 and is read on LL2 instead of LL3.

## Example 5.

Find the change in internal energy for air undergoing the following isentropic compression. $P_1 = 15$ psia, $P_2 = 60$ psia, $T_1 = 520$ deg. R, w = 13 lbs, $c_v = 0.1715$ btu/lb F, k = 1.40.

Answer 564 btu.

**Solution:**

From Table I write, $U_2 - U_1 = wc_v(T_2 - T_1)$ and $T_2 = T_1\left(\dfrac{P_2}{P_1}\right)^{\frac{k-1}{k}}$

Then $U_2 - U_1 = wc_v T_1\left[\left(\dfrac{P_2}{P_1}\right)^{\frac{k-1}{k}} - 1\right] = 13 \times 0.1715 \times 520$

$$\left[\left(\dfrac{60}{15}\right)^{\frac{1.4-1}{1.4}} - 1\right]$$

$$= 1160\left[4^{0.286} - 1\right]$$

Set left index of C opposite 4 on LL3 and move hairline over 0.286 on C. Read 1.486 on LL2 and subtract one from this, mentally obtaining 0.486. Set left index of C opposite 1160 on D and move hairline to 0.486 on C. Read 564 on D.

## EXERCISES

Solve the following exercises, using alternate methods when feasible.

160. Find $T_2$ for an isentropic process for which $T_1 = 560$, $P_1 = 14.7$, $P_2 = 49.25$, $k = 1.40$.

161. Find $P_2$ for an isentropic process for which $P_1 = 15$, $T_1 = 520$, $T_2 = 360$, $k = 1.30$

162. Find $P_2$ for a polytropic process for which $P_1 = 400$, $T_1 = 625$, $T_2 = 500$, $n = 1.05$.

163. Find n if $\dfrac{P_2}{P_1} = 7.5$ and $\dfrac{V_1}{V_2} = 4.4$

164. Compute the heat added to 1 lb. of air which undergoes a polytropic expansion with $n = 1.16$ from a pressure of 200 psia to 42 psia. The initial temperature is 900 deg. R. For air $c_v = 0.1715$ btu/lb F and $k = 1.40$.

165. Find $V_2$ for a polytropic compression of a gas if $n = 1.24$, $T_1 = 600$, $T_2 = 800$ and $V_1 = 16$.

## b. Equations Involving Natural Logarithms of Numbers.

Most thermodynamic equations involving logarithms can be reduced to one number multiplied by the natural logarithm of another. The solution of this type of problem is quite simple, since the natural log of a number can be read directly on the D scale opposite the number on one of the LL scales. If the number is greater than one, the logarithm will be positive and will have the decimal point indicated by the symbol at the right of the scale. If the number is less than one, the logarithm will be negative with the decimal point also indicated by the symbol. The multiplication process which follows is one of simply setting the left or right index of the C scale (whichever is appropriate) opposite the vluae fo the logarithm on the D scale and moving the hairline to the number by which the logarithm is to be multiplied. The final result is read on the D scale and given the appropriate sign and decimal point.

In the interest of accuracy and ease of computation, it is often an advantage to reduce the problem to its simplest form before performing the final operations. This will result in a minimum of effort in obtaining the solution. Example 6 illustrates this point.

## Example 6

Find the change in entropy per lb of gas resulting from a polytropic expansion for which n = 1.32 if $V_2 = 6V_1$. Assume $c_v = 0.18$ btu/lb F, and k = 1.39. Answer 0.0226 btu/deg. R.

### Solution:

Without reducing to its simplest form, the solution could be found as follows:

$$S_2 - S_1 = c_n \log_e \frac{T_2}{T_1} = c_v \left(\frac{k-n}{1-n}\right) \log_e \left(\frac{V_1}{V_2}\right)^{n-1} =$$
$$0.18 \left(\frac{1.39 - 1.32}{1 - 1.32}\right) \log_e(\tfrac{1}{6})^{0.32} = -0.0394 \log_e(\tfrac{1}{6})^{0.32}$$

Set left index of C opposite 6 on LL3 and move hairline to 0.32 on C. Read 0.5635 on LL/2. This is equal to $\frac{1}{6}$ raised to the 0.32 power. The logarithm of this is read under the hairline on the D scale, but with a negative sign, since it is for a number less than one.

From the symbol at the right of LL/2, it is clear that the logarithm read on D is −0.574. Set the right index of C under the hairline and move hairline to −0.0394 on C. Read 0.0226 on D.

### Alternate Solution:

By further mathematical manipulation, the solution can be reduced to the following, which is the preferred method.

$$S_2 - S_1 = -0.0394 \log_e (\tfrac{1}{6})^{0.32} = -0.32 \times 0.0394 \log_e \tfrac{1}{6} = 0.0126 \log_e 6$$

Set left index of C opposite 6 on LL3. Move hairline to 0.0126 on C and read 0.0226 on D.

### Example 7.

Find the work of an isothermal expansion of 7 lbs of hydrogen gas from a volume of 500 ft³ to 10,000 ft³. The temperature is 80 F (540 deg. R.) The gas constant for hydrogen is 772. Answer 11250 btu

### Solution:

Referring to Table I and noting that $\dfrac{P_1}{P_2} = \dfrac{V_2}{V_1}$ one may write

$$_1W_2 = \frac{wRT}{J} \log_e\frac{P_2}{P_1} = \frac{7 \times 772 \times 540}{778} \log_e\frac{V_2}{V_1} = \frac{7 \times 772 \times 540}{778} \log_e 20$$

Set 778 on C opposite 20 on LL3. Move hairline to 772 on C. Turn rule over and move 540 on CI under hairline. Move hairline to 7 on CF and read 11,250 on DF.

### Example 8.

Find the change in entropy for a constant pressure process in which 4 lbs of air are compressed at constant pressure from a volume of 50 ft³ to 10 ft³. $c_p$ for air $= 0.24$ btu/lb F. Answer $-1.545$ btu/deg. R.

### Solution:

Noting from Table I that $\dfrac{V_2}{V_1} = \dfrac{T_2}{T_1}$, the following can be written

$$S_2 - S_1 = wc_p \log_e \frac{T_2}{T_1} = 4 \times 0.24 \log_e \frac{10}{50} = -4 \times 0.24 \log_e 5$$

Set 4 on CI opposite 5 on LL3. Move hairline to 0.24 on C and read $-1.545$ on D.

### EXERCISES

166. Find the change in entropy per lb of air resulting from a polytropic expansion for which $n = 1.12$ if $V_2 = 18V_1$. Assume $c_v = 0.1715$ and $k = 1.4$.

167. Find the work of isothermal compression of 10 lbs of nitrogen from a volume of 36 ft³ to a volume of 4 ft³. The temperature is 60F. Gas constant for nitrogen $= 55.2$.

168. Find the heat added per lb of air undergoing an isothermal expansion from a pressure of 140 psia to 40 psia. The temperature is 600 deg.R. R = 53.3

169. Find the change in entropy for a constant volume extraction of 1000 btu of heat from 15 lbs of oxygen originally at 760 deg.R. $c_v$ for Oxygen = 0.155. btu/lb F.

170. For an isothermal compression the change in entropy of 3 lbs of carbon dioxide is −0.37 btu/deg.R. If the initial pressure is 15 psia, what is the final pressure? R for carbon dioxide is 35.1 ft/deg.R.

## HEAT TRANSFER

The mechanisms by which heat may be transferred are three, conduction, convection, and radiation. In this section each of these will be treated separately for the case of steady flow. The case of transient flow requires a high degree of mathematical training and is beyond the scope of this chapter.

### a. Conduction

Conduction may be defined as the flow of heat through a substance, the particles of which remain in a fixed position relative to each other. It is usually associated with the flow through solids although in the absence of convection currents heat can also be said to flow by conduction through liquids and gases. The flow of heat by conduction is directly proportional to a constant called the thermal conductivity multiplied by the temperature gradient and the cross sectional area perpendicular to flow, and inversely proportional to the distance through which it flows.

For a slab the flow may be expressed by the simple equation;

$$Q = \frac{kA\Delta t}{\tau} \qquad (1)$$

where

$Q$ = rate of flow of heat through the slab, btu/hr
$k$ = thermal conductivity of the slab material, btu/hr F ft
$A$ = cross sectional area of slab perpendicular to the flow of heat, ft$^2$
$\Delta t$ = temperature difference across the slab, F
$\tau$ = thickness of slab, ft

A problem of frequent occurrence in mechanical engineering is the determination of the flow of heat from an insulated pipe. For this case equation (1) must be modified to conform to the fact that the insulation is curved and that the area perpendicular to flow is greater at the outer surface.

The equation for this case is:

$$Q = \frac{2\pi k L \Delta t}{\log_e \dfrac{D_2}{D_1}} \tag{2}$$

where

$Q$ = heat loss, btu/hr
$L$ = length of pipe, ft
$\Delta t$ = temperature difference between inner and outer surface of the insulation, F
$D_2$ = outer diameter of insulation, ft
$D_1$ = inner diameter of insulation, ft

## Example 15.

Find the heat loss in btu per hr from a pipe of 8 inches outside diameter if it is 50 ft long and covered with 2 inches of insulation having a thermal conductivity of 0.035 btu/hr F ft. The inner temperature is 850 F and the outer temperature is 150 F. Answer 18,950 btu/hr

## Solution:

From equation 2 write

$$Q = \frac{2\pi \times 0.035 \times 50(850 - 150)}{\log_e \dfrac{12}{8}}$$

Divide 12 by 8 mentally to obtain 1.5. Set hairline over 1.5 on LL2 and read $\log_e 1.5 = 0.406$ on D. Subtract 150 from 850 mentally to obtain 700. Noting that $2 \times 50 = 100$, the problem reduces to $\pi\left(\dfrac{0.035 \times 70000}{0.406}\right)$. Set hairline to 70,000 on D and move 0.406 on C under hairline. Move hairline to 0.035 on C and read 6030 on D. This may be multiplied by $\pi$ by simple reading 18,950 on DF under the hairline.

## b. Convection

Heat flow by convection is an extremely complex subject since the mechanism of transfer is largely one of heat being conveyed from one portion of a fluid to another by physical mixing. The interaction of forces creating mixing and the consequent transfer of heat depends on many factors such as the density, specific heat, viscosity, thermal conductivity, temperature, and velocity of the fluid, as well as upon the geometry of the apparatus in which the fluid is contained. Many cases of practical importance have been studied but perhaps the most useful to the mechanical engineer is the rate of flow of heat to or from a fluid flowing inside a pipe or circular conduit. This problem has been studied by Dittus and Boelter of the University of California. Their work indicates that the rate of heat interchange between the inner surface of a pipe and a fluid flowing inside the pipe is proportional to a coefficient of conductance h. The rate of heat interchange in btu per hr may be computed by multiplying h by the inner surface area of the pipe and by the temperature difference between the inner surface and the fluid. The value of h is given by the equation

$$h = 0.023\frac{k}{D}\left(\frac{DV\rho}{\mu}\right)^{0.8}\left(\frac{\mu c_p}{k}\right)^n \tag{3}$$

where

$h$ = coefficient of conductance, btu/hr F ft²
$K$ = thermal conductivity of the fluid, btu/hr F ft²
$D$ = inside diameter of pipe, ft
$V$ = mean velocity of fluid inside pipe, ft/hr
$\rho$ = density of fluid, lbs/ft³
$\mu$ = viscosity of fluid, lbs/hr ft
$c_p$ = specific heat of the fluid at constant pressure, btu/lb F
$n$ = an exponent equal to 0.4 if the fluid is being heated and 0.3 if the fluid is being cooled.

The term $\dfrac{DV\rho}{\mu}$ is a dimensionless group called Reynold's number and occurs frequently in heat transfer and fluid flow calculations. It is sometimes very large and for this reason falls beyond the range of the LL3 scale on the slide rule making it necessary to apply special methods when raising it to a power. The term $\dfrac{\mu c_p}{k}$ is called Prandtl's number. It is usually quite small; often less than unity. Another group

called Nusselt's number can be formed as $\dfrac{hD}{k}$. The use of such dimensionless groups is widely employed in the theory of heat transfer and
fluid flow. These groups usually occur raised to some power thus making
the slide rule particularly applicable to their solution.

## Example 15:

Find the coefficient of conductance of superheated steam flowing to
a turbine with a velocity of 150 ft/sec. The inside diameter of the pipe
is 6 inches. The steam is under a pressure of 1,000 psia and a temperature of 800 F. The constants needed for the problem are k = 0.065
btu/hr F ft, $\rho$ = 1.451 lbs/ft³, $\mu$ = 0.104 lbs/ft hr $c_p$ = 0.61 btu/lb F.

Answer 3920 btu/hr F ft².

## Solution:

Since the steam is losing heat and therefore being cooled, the value
of $n$ will be 0.3. Hence, equation (3) becomes

$$h = 0.023 \underset{①}{\frac{0.065}{\left(\dfrac{6}{12}\right)}} \underset{②}{\left(\frac{6 \times 150 \times 3600 \times 1.451}{0.104}\right)^{0.8}} \underset{③}{\left(\frac{0.104 \times 0.61}{0.065}\right)^{0.3}}$$

The solution can best be obtained by treating the individual terms
of the equation indicated by the encircled numbers separately. Then
by the usual methods.

$$h = \underset{①}{0.00299} \times \underset{②}{45,200,000^{0.8}} \times \underset{③}{0.976^{0.3}}$$

Since 45,200,000 is beyond the range of the LL3 scale, it must be
divided into parts for the operation of raising to the 0.8 power. The
choice of division is not important so long as it is convenient and will
accomplish the desired result. The method which involves the least
work is to find the square root of the number, raise this to the 0.8
power, and square. Thus $45,200,000^{0.8} = 6720^{0.8} \times 6720^{0.8} = 1150^2 =$
1,323,000. To perform this operation, move the hairline to 45,200,000
on D and read its square root 6720 on $R_2$. Set right index of C to 6720
on LL3 and move hairline to 0.8 on C. Read 1150 on LL3. Set 1150 on
$R_1$ and read 1,323,000 on D. To find $0.976^{0.3}$ set left index of C opposite
0.976 on LL/1 and move hairline to 0.3 on C. Turn rule over and read
0.99275 on LL/0. Substituting these values into the equation for h gives

$$h = 0.00299 \times 1,323,000 \times 0.99275 = 3920 \quad btu/hr \quad F \quad ft^2$$

## c. Radiation

Heat may also be transferred from one surface to another by radiation. The mechanism of radiation differs from that of convection and conduction inasmuch as the heat is transferred without benefit of any intervening substance. It is radiated just as light except that the wave lengths are usually much greater. The general relation expressing the interchange of heat between two surfaces may be expressed by the equation.

$$Q = 0.173 \; F_A \; F_E \; A\left[\left(\frac{T_1}{100}\right)^4 - \left(\frac{T_2}{100}\right)^4\right] \tag{4}$$

where

$Q$ = heat transferred by radiation, btu/hr

$F_A$ = an angle factor which depends upon the geometry of the surfaces and their relative positions, dimensionless

$F_E$ = an emissivity factor which depends upon the ability of the surfaces to absorb and emit energy, dimensionless

$A$ = area of one of the surfaces, the choice of which depends upon the method of evaluating $F_A$, ft$^2$.

$T_1$ = absolute temperature of the warmer surface, deg. R. = 460 + F

$T_2$ = absolute temperature of the cooler surface, deg. R. = 460 + F

An illustrative example will serve to indicate the method of solution which will apply to problems of this type.

### Example 16:

Find the heat transferred per square ft of surface of one of two parallel plates if the angle factor is unity and if the emissivity factor is 0.154. The temperature of the two surfaces are 400 F and 60 F respectively.                                    Answer 126.5 btu/hr ft$^2$

### Solution:

$$Q = 0.173 \times 1 \times 0.154\left[\left(\frac{460 + 400}{100}\right)^4 - \left(\frac{460 + 60}{100}\right)^4\right] =$$
$$0.02665\left[8.60^4 - 5.20^4\right]$$

The values of $8.60^4$ and $5.20^4$ can be obtained by the use of the log log scales, by direct multiplication, or by the use of the R scales in conjunction with the C and D scales. The use of the log log scales is fast but is usually not very accurate. The use of the R scales is probably just as quick and much more accurate. The use of direct multiplication is not recommended.

Solution using the LL scales:

Set left index of C opposite 8.6 on LL3 and move hairline to 4 on C. Read 5500 on LL3. This is the value of $8.60^4$. By similar methods, find $5.20^4 = 730$. Then $Q = 0.0265(5500 - 730) = 0.02665 \times 4770 = 127.2$ btu/hr ft$^2$

Solution using the R scales:

Set right index of C opposite 8.6 on $R_2$. Read 74 on D. This is $8.60^2$. Move hairline to 74 on C and read 5480 on D. This is $8.60^4$. Set left index of C opposite 5.20 on $R_2$ and read 27.04 on D. Move hairline to 27.04 on C and read 731 on D. This is $5.20^4$. Then $Q = 0.02665(5480 - 731) = 0.02655 \times 4749 = 126.5$ btu/hr ft$^2$.

The latter solution is the more accurate of the two and to be preferred.

## d. Logarithmic Mean Temperature Difference

Various types of heat exchanger equipment are frequently employed in mechanical engineering applications. The most important of these are surface condensers, feedwater heaters, refrigeration condensers and evaporators, and counter and parallel flow heat exchangers. Their primary purpose is to transfer heat from one fluid to another across a barrier such as a pipe wall or some other separating surface. If the over-all coefficient of heat transfer is known, it is possible to compute a logarithmic mean temperature difference between the two fluids that can be multiplied by the surface area separating the fluids, and by the over-all coefficient, to obtain the rate of heat transfer.

Thus

$$Q = UA\Delta t_{LM} \tag{5}$$

where

$Q$ = rate of flow of heat from one fluid to the other, btu/hr

$U$ = over-all coefficient of heat transfer between the two fluids, btu/hr F ft$^2$

$\Delta t_{LM}$ = logarithmic mean temperature difference between the two fluids, F.

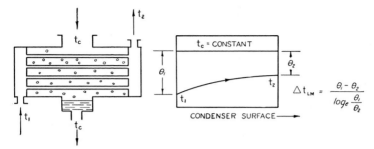

(a) *Steam condensers, feedwater heaters, refrigeration condensers.*

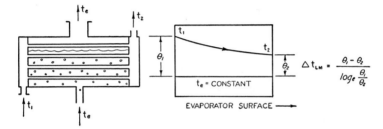

(b) *Refrigeration evaporators.*

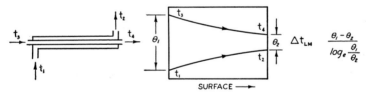

(c) *Parallel flow heat exchangers.*

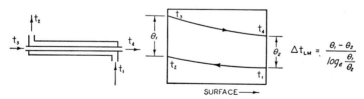

(d) *Counter flow heat exchangers.*

**Fig. 34—Temperature-surface curves for fluids passing through various types of heat exchanger equipment.** $\Delta t_{LM}$ = logarithmic mean temperature difference.

The relation between the two fluid temperatures as a function of the surface area for the various types of heat exchanger equipment is illustrated in Figure 34. The equation expressing the logarithmic mean temperature difference is the same in all cases and is given by the relation

$$\Delta t_{LM} = \frac{\Theta_1 - \Theta_2}{\log_e \dfrac{\Theta_1}{\Theta_2}} \tag{6}$$

where

$\Theta_1$ = temperature difference between the two fluids at inlet as indicated in Figure 34, F.

$\Theta_2$ = temperature difference between the two fluids at outlet as indicated in Figure 34, F.

For surface condensers, feedwater heaters, and refrigeration condensers and evaporators, the fluid which is condencing or evaporating remains at a constant temperature. Hence, only one of the fluids changes temperature as is clearly indicated in Figure 34, (a) and (b). Since equation (6) holds for all cases, it is important in engineering work. Its use in conjunction with equation (5) is illustrated by the three following examples.

## Example 16:

In a large steam surface condenser 5,000,000 lbs/hr of circulating water are raised in temperature from 60 F to 70 F. If the over-all coefficient of heat transfer is 720 btu/hr F ft² and if the condensing steam temperature is 79 F, what will be the required surface area? The specific heat of the water may be taken as 1 btu/lb F.    Answer 5190 ft²

## Solution:

From equations (5) and (6)

$$A = \frac{Q}{U \Delta t_{LM}} = \frac{Q \log_e \dfrac{\Theta_1}{\Theta_2}}{U(\Theta_1 - \Theta_2)}$$

Since the condensing steam temperature is constant, the value of $\Theta_1 - \Theta_2$ will be equal to the rise in temperature of the water. Hence, $Q = 5,000,000 (\Theta_1 - \Theta_2)$. Substitution of this value into the above equation gives

$$A = \frac{5,000,000}{720} \log_e \frac{79 - 60}{79 - 70} = \frac{5,000,000}{720} \log_e \frac{19}{9}$$

Set 9 on C opposite 19 on D and read 2.11 on D opposite right index of C. Move hairline over 2.11 on LL2 and slide 720 on C under hairline. Move hairline to 5,000,000 on C and read 5190 on D.

## Example 17:

A feedwater heater raises the temperature of 216,000 lbs of water per hr from 92 F to 175 F. If the over-all coefficient of heat transfer is 528 btu/hr F ft$^2$ and if the surface area is 769 ft$^2$, what will be the temperature of the condensing steam $t_c$?

## Solution:

From equations (5) and (6)

$$\Delta t_{LM} = \frac{\Theta_1 - \Theta_2}{\log_e \frac{\Theta_1}{\Theta_2}} = \frac{Q}{UA} \text{ or } \log_e \frac{\Theta_1}{\Theta_2} = \frac{UA(\Theta_1 - \Theta_2)}{Q}$$

Since the specific heat of water is unity, and since the condensing steam temperature is constant, $Q = 216,000(\Theta_1 - \Theta_2)$. Hence

$$\log_e \frac{\Theta_1}{\Theta_2} = \log_e \frac{t_c - 92}{t_c - 175} = \frac{528 \times 769}{216,000} = 1.88$$

or

$$\frac{t_c - 92}{t_c - 175} = e^{1.88}$$

The value of $e^{1.88}$ may be read directly on LL3 opposite 1.88 on D to obtain 6.55. Then

$$\frac{t_c - 92}{t_c - 175} = 6.55 \quad \text{or} \quad t_c = \frac{6.55 \times 175 - 92}{5.55} = 190 \text{ F}.$$

## Example 18:

A fluid having a specific heat of 0.65 btu/lb F flows through a counter flow heat exchanger at a rate of 520 lbs/hr. A second fluid having a specific heat of 0.72 btu/lb F flows through the exchanger at a rate of 714 lbs/hr. (a) If the first fluid enters at 560 F and leaves at 318 F what will be the temperature of the leaving second fluid if it enters at 194 F? (b) What will be the logarithmic mean temperature difference?

Answer 353 F, 161F.

**Solution:**

(a) The heat absorbed by the cooler fluid must equal that surrendered by the warmer fluid. Hence, the following heat balance can be written

$$520 \times 0.65(560 - 318) = 714 \times 0.72(t_2 - 194)$$

or

$$t_2 = \frac{520 \times 0.65 \times 242}{714 \times 0.72} + 194 = 159 + 194 = 353 \text{ F.}$$

(b) Referring to Figure 34, it is clear that $\Theta_1 = 560 - 353 = 270$ F, and $\Theta_2 = 318 - 194 = 122$ F. Then

$$\Delta t_{LM} = \frac{\Theta_1 - \Theta_2}{\log_e \dfrac{\Theta_1}{\Theta_2}} = \frac{207 - 122}{\log_e \dfrac{207}{122}} = \frac{85}{\log_e \dfrac{207}{122}}$$

Opposite 207 on D set 122 on C and read 1.696 opposite left index of C. Set hairline over 1.696 on LL2 and read 0.529 on D. This is $\log_e \dfrac{072}{122}$. Set hairline over 85 on D and move 0.529 on C under hairline. Read 1.61 on D opposite left index of C.

## EXERCISES

171. Find the heat loss in btu/hr from a pipe 42.8 ft long covered with insulation 1.5 inches thick having a thermal conductivity of 0.032 btu/hr F ft. The outside diameter of the insulation is 6 inches and the temperature drop across the insulation is 227 F.

172. Compute the coefficient of conductance of water flowing through a condenser if the tubes are $\frac{3}{4}$ inch inside diameter. The velocity of flow is 8 ft/sec. The physical constants are k = 0.35 btu/lb F ft, $\rho$ = 62.3 lbs/ft$^3$, $\mu$ = 2.37 lbs/ft hr, and $c_p$ = 1.00 btu/lb F.

173. Seven hundred lbs/hr of a fluid having a specific heat of 0.85 btu/lb F are passed in a heat exchanger counter flow to 600 lbs/hr of a fluid having a specific heat of 0.94 btu/lb F. If the first fluid enters at 500 F and leaves at 200 F, what will be the leaving temperature of the second fluid if it enters at 100 F? Compute the logarithmic mean temperature difference and the required area if the over-all coefficient of heat transfer U = 473 btu/hr F ft$^2$.

174. A surface condenser having a surface area of 40,000 ft² circulates 43,000,000 lbs of water per hr. The water increases in temperature from 70 F to 82 F. If the over-all coefficient of heat transfer U = 638 btu/hr F ft² what will be the temperature of the condensing steam?

175. A bare steam pipe passes through a room whose walls are at a temperature of 70 F. If the surface temperature of the pipe is 325 F find the rate at which heat is lost to the walls per square ft of pipe surface as a result of radiation. For this case assume $F_A = 1.00$ and $F_E = 0.90$.

## MACHINE DESIGN

In this section a few selected examples will be used to illustrate typical problems encountered in machine design practice. The problems are selected on the basis of their illustration of certain points regarding the operation of the slide rule rather than on frequency of occurrence.

### a. Rectangular and Polar Moments of Inertia, Radii of Gyration.

An important problem in machine design is the calculation of the stress induced in beams and machine members by the application of bending moments and torsional forces. The methods required for the complete solution of these problems are beyond the scope of this chapter. However, an important item that often enters into the solution, and which must be computed, is the moment of inertia of the cross section of the beam or machine member. When taken about a horizontal axis lying in the plane of the cross sectional area, and passing through its center, one obtains the rectangular moment of inertia I. When taken about an axis passing through the center of the cross sectional area, but perpendicular to the plane of the area, one obtains the polar moment of inertia Ip. Also of importance is the radius of gyration. It is that radius which, when squared and multiplied by the cross sectional area, gives the moment of inertia. In Table II, formulas for computing the two moments of inertia and their corresponding radii gyration for several widely employed cross sections are presented. A few examples of their solution, illustrating principally the use of the K and R scales follow.

## TABLE II

### Rectangular and polar moment of inertia of plane cross sections. Radii of gyration.

| Section | Rectangular Moment of Inertia I | Rectangular Radius of Gyration R | Polar Moment of Inertia $I_P$ | Polar Radius of Gyration $R_P$ |
|---|---|---|---|---|
| (rectangle, $h$, $b$) | $\dfrac{bh^3}{12}$ | $\dfrac{h}{\sqrt{12}}$ | $\dfrac{bh(b^2+h^2)}{12}$ | $\sqrt{\dfrac{b^2+h^2}{12}}$ |
| (hollow rectangle, $H$, $B$, $b$, $h$) | $\dfrac{BH^3-bh^3}{12}$ | $\sqrt{\dfrac{BH^3-bh^3}{12(BH-bh)}}$ | $\dfrac{B^3H+BH^3-b^3h-bh^3}{12}$ | $\sqrt{\dfrac{B^3H+HB^3-b^3h-bh^3}{12(Bh-bh)}}$ |
| (circle, $d$) | $\dfrac{\pi d^4}{64}$ | $\dfrac{d}{4}$ | $\dfrac{\pi d^4}{32}$ | $\dfrac{d}{\sqrt{8}}$ |
| (hollow circle, $D$, $d$) | $\dfrac{\pi(D^4-d^4)}{64}$ | $\dfrac{\sqrt{D^2+d^2}}{4}$ | $\dfrac{\pi(D^4-d^4)}{32}$ | $\sqrt{\dfrac{D^2+d^2}{8}}$ |
| (ellipse, $a$, $b$) | $\dfrac{\pi a^3 b}{64}$ | $\dfrac{a}{4}$ | $\dfrac{\pi a^3 b}{32}$ | $\dfrac{a}{\sqrt{8}}$ |

## Example 19:

Find the polar moment of inertia and polar radius of gyration of the rectangular cross section in Table II if h and b are 2.22 and 1.50 inches respectively. Answer 1.99 in$^4$, 0.774 in

## Solution:

Write the polar moment of inertia as

$$I_p = \frac{bh(b^2 + h^2)}{12} = \frac{b^3h}{12}\left[1 + \left(\frac{h}{b}\right)^2\right] = \frac{1.50^3 \times 2.22}{12}\left[1 + \left(\frac{2.22}{1.50}\right)^2\right]$$

Opposite 2.22 on D set 1.50 on C. Opposite left index of C read 1.48 on D. Move hairline to 1.48 on C and read 2.19 on D. This is $\left(\frac{2.22}{1.50}\right)^2$. Add one to 2.19 mentally obtaining 3.19 and set hairline over 3.19 on D. Move slide so that 12 on C rests under hairline and then move hairline to 2.22 on C and read 0.59 on D. Find 1.50$^3$ by setting hairline to 1.5 on D and reading 3.375 on K. Set right index of C opposite 0.59 on D. Move hairline to 3.375 on C and read the answer 1.99 on D.

Write the polar radius of gyration as

$$R = \sqrt{\frac{b^2 + h^2}{12}} = b\sqrt{\frac{1 + \left(\frac{h}{b}\right)^2}{12}} = 1.50\sqrt{\frac{1 + \left(\frac{2.22}{1.50}\right)^2}{12}}$$

By the same methods as above find $1 + \left(\frac{2.22}{1.50}\right)^2 = 3.19$. Set hairline opposite 3.19 on D. Move 12 on C under hairline and move hairline over left index of C. Read 0.5155 on $R_2$. Set left index of C to 0.5155 on D and move hairline to 1.5 on C. Read the answer 0.774 on D. As a check $R_p^2 \times bh = I_p$. Hence, $0.774^2 \times 2.22 \times 1.50 = 1.99$.

## Example 20:

Find the rectangular radius of gyration of the hollow rectangular section if B, H, b and h are 3.2, 4.6, 1.8 and 2.6 respectively. Answer 1.50 in$^2$

## Solution:

For this problem it is easiest to solve for each member under the radical separately using the R scales in conjunction with the CI and D scales. Thus

$$BH^3 = 3.2 \times 4.6^3 = 3.2 \times 4.6 \times 4.6^2 = 312$$

To perform the above operations, set hairline opposite 4.6 on $R_2$ and read 21.16 on D. This is $4.6^2$. Slide 4.6 on CI under hairline and then move hairline to 3.2 on C. Read 312 on D.

$$bh^3 = 1.8 \times 2.6 \times 2.6^2 = 31.65$$

Set hairline over 2.6 on $R_1$ and read 6.76 on D. This is $2.6^2$. Slide 2.6 on CI under hairline and move hairline to 1.8 on C to obtain 31.65 on D. The denominator under the radical is found in the usual manner.

$$12(BH - bh) = 12(3.2 \times 4.6 - 1.8 \times 2.6) = 12(14.72 - 4.68) = 124.8$$

then

$$R = \sqrt{\frac{312 - 31.65}{124.8}} = \sqrt{\frac{280.35}{124.8}} = 1.50$$

Set 124.8 on C opposite 280.35 on D. Move hairline to left index of C and read 1.50 on $R_1$.

## Example 21:

Find the width of an elliptical section of height 2.9 inches which will give a rectangular moment of inertia equal to 0.584 in⁴.   Answer 1.60 in

## Solution:

$$I = \frac{\pi a^3 b}{64} \quad \text{and} \quad a = \sqrt[3]{\frac{64\,I}{\pi b}} = \sqrt[3]{\frac{64 \times 0.584}{\pi \times 2.9}} = 1.60$$

Set $\pi$ on C opposite 64 on D. Move hairline to 2.9 on CI and slide 0.584 on CI under hairline. Opposite left index of C read 4.1 on D. Set hairline over 4.1 on K and read $\sqrt[3]{4.1} = 1.60$ on D.

## b. Belt Length and Tension

The use of the S scale together with certain other manipulations may be illustrated by the equations for belt length and belt tension.

Figure 35 is an illustration of two pulleys over which an open belt is stretched.

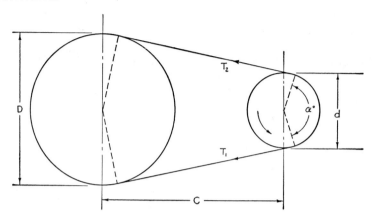

**Fig. 35—Pulleys with Open Belt.**

The equation for length of belt required is

$$L = \sqrt{4C^2 - (D - d)^2} + \pi\left(\frac{D + d}{2}\right) + (D - d)\sin^{-1}\frac{D - d}{2C} \quad (7)$$

where $\sin^{-1}\dfrac{D - d}{2C}$ must be in radians and

L = belt length, in
D = diameter of larger pulley, in
d = diameter of smaller pulley, in
C = distance between pulley centers, in

The angle of contact between belt and smaller pulley is given by the expression

$$\alpha^\circ = 180 - 2\sin^{-1}\frac{D - d}{2C} \quad (8)$$

Expressed in radians $\alpha = \dfrac{\alpha^\circ}{57.3}$ radians.

The tension developed by the tight side of the belt in terms of that on the loose side is

$$T_1 = T_2 e^{\mu\alpha} \quad (9)$$

In equation (9)

$T_1$ = tension on tight side, lbs
$T_2$ = tension on loose side, lbs
$\mu$ = coefficient of friction between belt and pulley
$\alpha$ = angle of contact between belt and smaller pulley, radians

The effective torque for producing power will be $(T_1 - T_2)\dfrac{d}{2}$ inch lbs
so that the horsepower developed will be

$$hp = \frac{2\pi N(T_1 - T_2)d}{12 \times 33{,}000 \times 2} = \frac{Nd(T_1 - T_2)}{126{,}000} \tag{10}$$

where

N = revolutions per minute of the smaller pulley
d = diameter of the smaller pulley, in

## Example 22:

(a) Compute the required length of an open belt to stretch between two pulleys 60 inches apart if their diameters are 22 and 8 inches. (b) Compute the angle of contact of the belt on the smaller pulley in degrees and in radians. (c) If the belt is to transmit 20 hp and if the smaller pulley is to operate at 800 rpm, what will be the tension on the tight and loose sides of the belt. Assume $\mu = 0.30$.

Answer 168 in, 166.6 deg., 2.91 radians, 676 lbs, 282 lbs

## Solution:

(a)

$$L = \sqrt{4 \times 60^2 - (22 - 8)^2} + \pi\left(\frac{22 + 8}{2}\right) + (22 - 8)\sin^{-1}\left(\frac{22 - 8}{2 \times 60}\right)$$

this may easily be reduced to the following

$$L = 14 \underbrace{\sqrt{\left(\frac{120}{14}\right)^2 - 1}}_{①} + \underbrace{\pi \times 15}_{②} + \underbrace{14 \sin^{-1}\frac{14}{120}}_{③}$$

① Set 14 on C opposite 120 on D and read 8.57 on D opposite right index of C. Move hairline to 8.57 on C and read 73.5 on D. This is $\left(\dfrac{120}{14}\right)^2$. Subtract one from this mentally to obtain 72.5. Set hairline over 72.5 on D and read 8.51 on $R_2$. Set right index of C opposite 8.52 on D and move hairline to 14 on C. Read 119.2 on D. This is the value of the first term.

② Set hairline to 15 on D and read $\pi \times 15 = 47.1$ on DF.

③ Divide 14 by 120 and obtain 0.1167. Set hairline to 0.1167 on C and read 6.70 degrees on S. This is $\sin^{-1} \dfrac{14}{120}$ in degrees. To find the number of radians set hairline to 6.70 on D and slide 57.3 (marked R on C scale) to hairline. Read 0.117 on D opposite left index of C. Multiply by 14 by moving hairline to 14 on C. Read 1.64 on D. This is the third term. Adding the three terms gives

$$L = 119.2 + 47.1 + 1.64 = 167.94 \cong 168 \text{ in.}$$

(b) The angle of contact will be

$$\alpha° = 180 - 2 \sin^{-1} \frac{D - d}{2C} = 180 - 2 \sin^{-1} \frac{14}{120} = 180 - 2 \times 6.70$$
$$= 166.6 \text{ deg.}$$

Set hairline to 166.6 on D and move 57.3 (R on C scale) to hairline. Read $\alpha = 2.91$ radians on D opposite right index of C.

(c) From equation (10) the difference in belt tensions can be computed

$$T_1 - T_2 = \frac{126,000 \text{ hp}}{Nd} = \frac{126,000 \times 20}{800 \times 8} = 394 \text{ lbs}$$

also

$$\frac{T_1}{T_2} = e^{\mu a} = e^{0.30 \times 2.91} = e^{0.873}$$

Set hairline to 0.873 on D and read $e^{0.873} = 2.393$ on LL2. Then

$$T_1 = 2.393 T_2 = 2.393(T_1 - 394)$$

or

$$T_1 = \frac{2.393 \times 394}{1.393} = 676 \text{ lbs}$$

and

$$T_2 = 676 - 394 = 282 \text{ lbs}$$

## c. Displacement and Velocity of the Piston of a Reciprocating Engine

In Figure 36 is represented a crank and connecting rod similar to that employed on reciprocating engines for the conversion of rectilinear motion to rotary motion. With this mechanism two important problems arise. These are the determination of piston displacement and piston velocity as a function of crank angle Θ. The two quantities may be expressed by the equations:

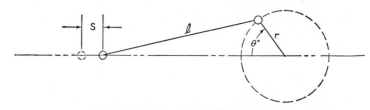

**Fig. 36—Connecting Rod and Crank.**

$$S = r(1 - \cos\theta + \tfrac{1}{2}\tfrac{r}{l}\sin^2\theta + \tfrac{1}{8}\left(\tfrac{r}{l}\right)^3\sin^4\theta + \cdots) \qquad (11)$$

$$V = 2\pi Nr(\sin\theta + \tfrac{r}{l}\sin\theta\cos\theta + \tfrac{1}{2}\left(\tfrac{r}{l}\right)^3\sin^3\theta\cos\theta +) \qquad (12)$$

where

$S$ = piston displacement, ft or inches
$l$ = length of piston rod, same units as $S$
$r$ = radius of crank, same units as $S$
$\theta$ = crank angle, degrees
$V$ = piston velocity, ft/min or in/min depending on units chosen for $l$ and $r$
$N$ = revolutions per minute

Equations (11) and (12) may be solved with a high degree of accuracy by including the last term, but in general this may be neglected.

**Example 23:**

(a) Find the piston displacement in inches and piston velocity in ft/min for an internal combustion engine operating at 3000 rpm if $\theta = 68$ degrees, $l = 8$ in, and $r = 3$ in. (b) Solve the same problem, neglecting the last term, if $\theta = 185$ degrees.
Answer 2.38 in, 4950 ft/min, 5.99 in, $-$ 252 ft/min.

**Solution:**

(a)

$$S = 3[1 - \cos 68° + \tfrac{1}{2} \times \tfrac{3}{8} \sin^2 68° + \tfrac{1}{8} (\tfrac{3}{8})^3 \times \sin^4 68° + \cdots]$$

and

$$V = \frac{2\pi \times 3000 \times 3}{12} [\sin 68° + \tfrac{3}{8} \sin 68° \cos 68° + \tfrac{1}{2}(\tfrac{3}{8})^3 \sin^3 68°$$
$$\cos 68° + \cdots]$$

Using the S scale in conjunction with the C scale both the sin and cos of 68° are found to be 0.934 and 0.3745 respectively. The remaining steps are simple and need not be explained in detail.

$$S = 3[1 - 0.3745 + \tfrac{3}{16} \times 0.934^2 + \tfrac{1}{8}(\tfrac{3}{8})^3 \times 0.934^4]$$

$$= 3[1 - 0.3745 + 0.1636 + 0.00406] = 2.38 \text{ in.}$$

$$V = 4615[0.934 + \tfrac{3}{8} \times 0.934 \times 0.3745 + \tfrac{1}{2} \times (\tfrac{3}{8})^3 \times 0.934^3 \times 0.3745]$$

$$= 4615[0.934 + 0.1312 + 0.00805] = 4950 \text{ ft/min.}$$

(b)

Since sin 185° = −sin 5° and since cos 185° = −cos 5° one may find from the ST and S scales in conjunction with the C scale the following:

$$\text{Sin } 185° = -\sin 5° = -0.0871 \text{ (from ST scale)}$$
$$\text{Cos } 185° = -\cos 5° = -0.996 \quad \text{(from S scale)}$$

then

$$S = 3[1 + 0.996 + \tfrac{1}{2} \times \tfrac{3}{8} \times 0.0871^2] = 5.99 \text{ in.}$$
$$V = 4615[-0.0871 + \tfrac{3}{8} \times 0.0871 \times 0.996] = -252 \text{ ft/min.}$$

The negative sign for velocity in this case simply means that the piston in Figure 1 is traveling form right to left.

## EXERCISES

176. Compute the rectangular moment of inertia and rectangular radius of gyration of a circular annulus if D = 4.5 in and d = 3.44 in. Check moment of inertia by using radius of gyration and area.

177. Compute the polar moment of inertia and polar radius of gyration of the hollow rectangular cross section if B = 4.3, H = 6.4, b = 2.7 and h = 4.8. Check moment of inertia using radius of gyration and area.

178. Find the length of belt required for two pulleys 72 inches apart if one pulley is 48 inches in diameter and the other is 8 inches in diameter.

179. Find the angle of contact for the smaller pulley in problem 178 both in degrees and in radians. If the pulley is to transmit 15 hp at 800 rpm what will be the tension on the two sides of the belt assuming $\mu = 0.20$

180. Find the piston displacement and velocity for a steam engine operating at 150 rpm if $\theta = 80$ degrees, $1 = 3$ ft and $r = 0.75$ ft. Solve the same problem for $\theta = 12$ degrees.

*Chapter 9*

# APPLICATIONS TO ELECTRICAL ENGINEERING

*by* B. A. FISHER, B.S., M.S., E.E.

**Purpose.** The purpose of this chapter is to present a few of the situations in which the Frederick Post Versalog slide rule offers unusual advantages to the Electrical Engineer, and in certain cases to describe the methods to be used in order that the maximum of advantage may be realized. Detailed attention will be given to the uses of the trigonometric scales. It is in that area that the Electrical Engineer will find his greatest satisfaction with this slide rule but the benefits can be realized only if proper operational procedures are mastered. A small investment in time spent at the outset in learning such procedures will pay off handsomely in the long run.

## THE C AND D SCALES

In Electrical Engineering as in other fields, the bulk of the every day routine work is done with the C and D scales. It is worth while to devote considerable attention to the procedures outlined in the earlier chapters of this manual for their most economical use, including combined operations with the $\pi$-folded C and D scales. Facility in handling proportions is also of great value in Electrical Engineering. Illustrations follow.

**Use of Proportion Methods in Problems of Resistance Changes Resulting from Temperature Changes.** Resistances of metallic conductors increase with increasing temperature. The formula representing this change is most conveniently expressed as a proportion, as follows:

$$\frac{R_2}{R_1} = \frac{234.5 + t_2}{234.5 + t_1}$$

where $R_2$ is resistance at centigrade temperature $t_2$ and $R_1$ is resistance at $t_1$. The constant 234.5 is suitable for "standard annealed copper." Other constants are required for other materials. The slide rule C and D scales are very convenient for the solution of any proportion.

**Example:** The field winding of a motor has 56 ohms resistance at an ambient temperature of 25° C. After full load operation for two hours the resistance is found to be 74.3 ohms. What average temperature was reached by the winding?

### Solution:

$$\frac{74.3}{56} = \frac{234.5 + t_2}{259.5}$$

The slide rule is used to find $234.5 + t_2$. The procedure using proportion is to bring 743 on the C scale in register with 56 on the D scale. Then set the hairline to 2595 on D and read $234.5 + t_2 = 344.5$ on C. $t_2 = 344.5 - 234.5 = 110°C$.

Any one of the four quantities $R_2$, $R_1$, $t_2$, or $t_1$ may, of course, be the unknown.

For slide rule users who have continually to make this type of calculation, it is recommended that auxiliary scales be etched on the slide rule adjacent to the C and D scales as follows:

At 214.5 on C and D, put a mark and label it $-20°$; at 234.5, another mark labeled 0°; at 254.5, a mark labeled 20°C; and on up every 20° to temperatures as high as required. With such auxiliary scales it becomes possible to make the calculation direct in centigrade degrees without the irksome requirement of adding and subtracting 234.5.

For materials other than standard annealed copper, the constant 234.5 must be replaced as follows:

| | |
|---|---|
| Hard drawn copper | 242 |
| Commercial aluminum | 236.5 |
| Silver | 243 |
| Platinum | 313 |
| Nickel | 230 |
| Mercury | 236.5 |
| Tungsten | 202 |

### EXERCISES

181. A 100 watt tungsten filament lamp operating at 2,200° C has a resistance of 132 ohms. What is its resistance just after switching on, before the temperature has had a chance to rise above room temperature of 20° C?

182. The "cold," (30° C), resistance of an armature winding of copper is 0.0345 ohms. If, under full load operation, the temperature is expected to rise 50°, what is the expected operating resistance?

**Use of $\pi$-Folded Scales for Circular-Mil Areas of Rectangular Conductors.** The cross-sectional area expressed in circular-mils of a rectangular conductor is found as follows:

Area $= \dfrac{4\ a\ b}{\pi}$ circular mils, where a and b are the cross-section dimensions in mils.

**Example:** A rectangular rotorconductor in an induction motor has a cross section $\frac{1}{4}$ inch by $\frac{1}{2}$ inch. Find the cross section in circular mils.

$$\text{Area} = \frac{4 \times 250 \times 500}{\pi} = 159,100 \text{ circular mils.}$$

Here the important thing is to make economical use of the $\pi$-folded scales. In this case it is only necessary, after noting that $4 \times 250 = 1000$, to set the hairline to 5 on the DF scale and read 1591 on D under the hairline.

### EXERCISE

183. What is the cross section in circular mils of a bus bar 0.25 inches thick and 3.5 inches wide?

### THE R SCALES

The square root scales are of particular value to the Electrical Engineer. Examples of their uses follow:

**Copper Loss in Wires and Machines when the Current and the Resistance Are Known.**

**Example:** For a current of 120 amperes in a resistance of 0.076 ohms, to find the power dissipated using $P = I^2R$: Set hairline to 120 on R; place 76 on CI under hairline; read result on D under left index of slide, $P = 1094$ watts.

**Copper Loss in Wires and Machines when the Potential Drop and the Resistance Are Known.**

**Example:** For a voltage drop of 9.11 volts in a resistance of 0.076 ohms, to find the power dissipated using $P = E^2/R$: Set hairline to 911 on R; set 76 on C under hairline; read result on D under left index of slide, $P = 1092$ watts.

Note that in these operations greater accuracy is possible than with slide rules employing the conventional "A" and "B" scales; and setting of the decimal point is simplified.

**Calculations Relating to Circuits Possessing Resonant Qualities.** It is frequently necessary to evaluate $\sqrt{LC}$, $\sqrt{L/C}$, and $\sqrt{C/L}$ where L and C are inductance and capacitance (sometimes per unit length of circuit). Here the quantity under the radical is evaluated by the usual methods using the C and D scales. A final setting of the hairline transfers this quantity to the R scale where the square root is read.

The slide rule settings concerned require no illustration at this stage of the instruction but because of the orders of magnitudes usually involved, the decimal point must be located with care.

**Example:** L = 150 microhenries. C = 80 micro-micro-farads. To find $\sqrt{LC}$

$$\sqrt{LC} = \sqrt{1.5 \times 10^{-4} \times 0.8 \times 10^{-10}} = \sqrt{1.2 \times 10^{-14}} = 1.095 \times 10^{-7}$$

It is to be noted that *even* powers of ten were factored from the numbers in order to bring the decimal points close to the first digit and to facilitate taking mentally the square root of the power of ten.

**Root-mean-square Value of Non-sinusoidal Current or Voltage.** When the r.m.s. values of the harmonic components are known, the r.m.s. value of the non-sinusoidal function may be found from

$$E = \sqrt{E^2_1 + E^2_2 + E^2_3 + \text{etc.}}$$

Here the R scale may be used with the D scale. Full advantage is gained from the superior accuracy of this slide rule over those having A and B scales.

**Power Factor for Phase Angles Less than 10 Degrees.** We may use the approximation

$$\cos x = 1 - \frac{x^2}{2}$$

Cosine scales on slide rules are so condensed below 10 degrees as to render accurate interpolation difficult. When a cosine in this range must be known accurately, as is often the case in power factor problems, the approximation given above may be used to advantage.

x is the phase angle in radians. The upper limit at which this approximation should be applied is $10° = 0.1745$ radians. Let us calculate cos (0.1745 radians) according to the approximation and compare the result with a five-place table. The error made will be the maximum, since for smaller values of x the method becomes more accurate.

$x = 0.1745$ radians.
$x^2 = 0.03045$ radians, using the R scale in the usual way with the D scale.
$x^2/2 = 0.01523$.
$1 - x^2/2 = 0.98477 = \cos 10°$ approximately.

From a five place table $\cos 10° = 0.98481$. The difference is $0.00004$.

**Circular-mil Areas of Round Conductors.** Area $= D^2$ circular mils where D is diameter of wire in mils.

**Example:** A micrometer caliper shows the diameter of a round wire to be 0.1019 inches. Find the area in circular mils.

Area $= 101.9^2 = 10,380$ circular mils.

This calculation is made with the help of the R scale in the usual way.

### EXERCISES

184. The potential drop across a load is indicated by a voltmeter reading to be 232 volts. The voltmeter resistance is 30,000 ohms, as is the resistance of the potential coil of the wattmeter. What "potential coil loss" error must be subtracted from the wattmeter reading?

185. Calculate the copper loss in a field winding of 57 ohms resistance if the current is 0.89 amperes.

186. Determine the surge impedance of a radio-frequency transmission line whose inductance per foot of line is $L = 304,500$ micro-micro-henries and whose capacitance per foot is $C = 3.385$ micro-micro-farads. $(Z_o = \sqrt{L/C})$

187. What capacitance C in micro-micro-farads is required to tune a 200 micro-henry coil to a frequency of one million cycles per second?

$$\left( C = \frac{1}{(2\pi f)^2 L} \right)$$

188. Measurements with a "wave analyzer" on a nonsinusoidal voltage wave indicate the following components to be present: $E_1 = 287$, $E_2 = 57$, $E_3 = 22$, $E_4 = 9$, $E_5 = 0$, $E_6 = 0$, $E_7 = 2$, all being root-mean-square voltages. Find the root-mean-square value of the wave.

189. Find cos 1.62 degrees.

190. Find the circular-mil area of a stranded wire made of 7 strands of circular conductor, each strand having a diameter of 0.0808 inches.

## THE L SCALE

The L scale is useful for calculation of logarithmic power ratios in terms of decibels by either of the formulae:

$$\text{d.b.} = 10 \log_{10}\frac{P_2}{P_1} \quad \text{or} \quad \text{d.b.} = 20 \log_{10}\frac{V_2}{V_1}$$

**Example:** Let $\frac{P_2}{P_1} = 460$. Set the hairline to 460 on D. Read the mantissa of $\log_{10} 460$ under the hairline on L, obtaining 0.663. Mentally determine the characteristic of the logarithm and add it to the mantissa, thus: 2.663. Then d.b. = 26.63. If data from the same physical situation had been in terms of voltage ratio, this would have been $\frac{V_2}{V_1} = 21.45$. Proceeding as before, $\log_{10} 21.45 = 1.3315$ or d.b. = 26.63

Sometimes it is necessary to calculate the power ratio corresponding to a known number of decibels change in power level. This relationship is expressed by the equation

$$\frac{P_2}{P_1} = \text{Log}_{10}^{-1}\left(\frac{\text{d.b.}}{10}\right)$$

**Example:** d.b. = 26.63. d.b./10 = 2.663 = $\log_{10}\frac{P_2}{P_1}$. Set hairline to 663 on L. Read under the hairline on D the digits 460 representing

$P_2/P_1$. The decimal point is placed after the third digit because the characteristic of the logarithm 2.663 is 2.

If voltage ratio is desired from the above data, $\dfrac{V_2}{V_1} = \sqrt{\dfrac{P_2}{P_1}} =$

$\sqrt{460} = 21.45$ may be obtained from the D and R scales in the usual way.

## EXERCISES

191. In carrier-frequency telephone repeater input circuits one-half of the received power is lost in a line-matching resistor. What is the d.b. power loss in this case?

192. In a radio frequency amplifier the input voltage is 0.2 volts. The output voltage is 45 volts. Find the d.b. voltage gain.

193. A 600 ohm low pass filter designed to "cut off" at 2,000 cycles per second accepts 6 microwatts power at this frequency, whereas a termination of 600 ohms would accept 1 milliwatt. What loss in d.b. is introduced by the filter, at this frequency?

## THE LL SCALES

The unique log-log scales of the Post Versalog slide rule are of great value in a variety of electrical problems. These scales have an arrangement and coverage that make them unsurpassed for the following calculations:

**Exponential Decay Terms in the Solution of Transient Problems.** These terms take the form $e^{-kt}$ where the function must be evaluated for a series of values of the time t. The exponent kt is first determined for different values of the time t. The hairline is then successively set to the values of kt on the D scale and the corresponding results for $e^{-kt}$ read from the appropriate level of the reciprocal log log scales as determined from the right end zone symbols.

**Examples:**

| kt | | $e^{-kt}$ | |
|---|---|---|---|
| 0.008 | on D gives | 0.9920 | on LL/0 |
| 0.08 | on D gives | 0.9231 | on LL/1 |
| 0.8 | on D gives | 0.4495 | on LL/2 |
| 8.0 | on D gives | 0.00034 | on LL/3 |

Note that with this slide rule the exponential term may be found with good accuracy from 0.999 down to 0.0000454, for values of the exponent from 0.001 to 10.0. For times on the transient earlier than $kt = 0.001$ it is possible with a maximum error of about 5 parts in one million to use the LL/0 scale for the range $kt = 0.001$ to $0.0001$. This is done by assuming another 9 to be inserted between the decimal point and the numerals in the numbering of the LL/0 scale.

Thus: $e^{-.0008} = 0.99920$. Similarly,
$$e^{-.00008} = 0.999920, \text{ etc.}$$

Thus there is no limit to re-cycling on the LL/4 scale toward unity. Two digits beyond the 9's will be accurate.

**Hysteresis Loss in Iron.** The loss is expressed as

$$P_h = K_h f\, B_m^x \text{ where}$$
$P_h$ = hysteresis loss in watts per pound of iron;
$K_h$ = a coefficient;
$f$ = frequency in cycles per second;
$B_m$ = maximum flux density in kilo-lines per square inch;
$x$ = the "Steinmetz exponent."

**Example:** $P_h = 0.6$, $K_h = 1.2 \times 10^{-5}$, $B_m = 65$, $f = 60$. Find $x$:
$$0.6 = 1.2 \times 10^{-5} \times 60 \times 65^x.$$
$$65^x = 833.$$

The question is, to what power must 65 be raised to give 833? Set the hairline to 65 on LL3; set left index of C to hairline; move hairline to 833 on LL3; read $x = 1.61$ under hairline on C.

The inverse of this problem arises when $P_h$ is unknown and $x$ is known. As an illustration, suppose $x = 1.61$, $B_m = 70$, and other data as in the previous example. Find $P_h$.

$$P_h = 1.2 \times 10^{-5} \times 60 \times 70^{1.61}$$

Evaluate $70^{1.61} = 937$ as follows:
Set hairline to 70 on LL3; set left index of C to hairline; move hairline to 1.61 on C; read 937 under hairline on LL3. Then
$$P_h = 1.2 \times 10^{-5} \times 60 \times 937 = 0.675 \text{ watts per pound at 60 cycles.}$$

**Emission of Electrons from Cathodes.** Calculations in this field frequently require raising a number to a power. The exponent is frequently 1.5 or 4.0. Since the method of solution is the same as that given under the heading Hysteresis Loss in Iron, details will not be repeated.

## EXERCISES

194. A 3 micro-farad capacitor charges through an 800,000 ohm resistor from a 400 volt source. Find the current at t = 2.4 seconds.

$$\text{(Formula:} \quad i = \frac{E}{R}e^{-t/RC})$$

195. Repeat the previous exercise when t = 4.8 seconds.

196. Repeat for t = 0.048 seconds.

197. An iron core has a hysteresis loss of 0.5 watts per pound at 60 cycles and $B_m = 65$. x is known to be 1.6. Find $K_h$.

198. The plate current in a certain vacuum tube follows the law: $I = 1.2 \times 10^{-5} E^{1.5}$. If the voltage E is 200, find I.

## THE TRIGONOMETRIC SCALES

The Post Versalog slide rule includes trigonometric scales which have been designed with especial attention to the needs of the Electrical Engineer. In the past considerable resistance to the use of so-called "vector scales" has existed on the part of students of Electrical Engineering, and even among instructors in this field. With slide rules existing prior to the Post Versalog rule, this resistance was well founded because there was no simple way to keep track of basic operations of multiplication and division by sin θ, cos θ, and tan θ. So much care was required to avoid operational errors due to misuse of the scales that the many advantages possible with properly designed trigonometric scales were greatly reduced.

Any user of this slide rule who has mastered the use of the C and CI scales for multiplication and division can multiply and divide by sin θ, cos θ, or tan θ with the same assurance he feels in using the C and CI scales. Only one simple rule has to be observed: *If a trigonometric scale is black, use it as you would a C scale; if red, use it as you would a CI scale.* Electrical Engineers will find that their Post Versalog slide rules permit solution of alternating current problems with a freedom from operational errors not possible with other slide rules.

The non-specialized uses of the trigonometric scales have been treated elsewhere in this manual. The reader should, before proceeding, review the descriptions and fundamental uses of the trigonometric scales there given.

It is again urged that the slide rule user cultivate the habit of thinking of the four *black* trigonometric scales as though they were in fact C scales, and of the two *red* trigonometric scales as though they were in fact CI scales. Such is indeed the fundamental nature of these scales, a simple fact which makes their uses quite as simple as those of the C and CI scales. An example will illustrate this point.

**Example:** A load of 4,000 kilowatts draws current at a lag angle of 25 degrees. (a) Find the number of kilovolt-amperes. (b) Find the reactive power drawn from the line.

**Solution:**

$$(a) \quad \text{kva} = \frac{\text{kw}}{\cos \Theta} = \frac{4,000}{\cos 25°} = 4,415$$

Here cos Θ is 0.906 as may be verified by setting the hairline to 25° on the Cos scale and reading 0.906 on C. It is unnecessary to take the additional step of evaluating cos Θ, and then dividing 4,000 by 0.906. Instead, the hairline is set to 4,000 on D, the slide moved to bring 25° on the Cos scale under the hairline, and the result is read on D under the right index of C. Note that the setting used is exactly the same as that used in evaluating $\frac{4,000}{0.906}$ with the C scale. Thus, the division was performed by using the Cos scale as though it were a C scale.

$$(b) \quad \text{kvar} = (\text{kw}) \tan \Theta = 4,000 \tan 25° = 1,865$$

Tan 25° = 0.466, which may be verified by setting the hairline to 25° on T (black) and reading 0.466 on C. This step is unnecessary. Instead, set right index of T (black) to 4,000 on D and set hairline over 25° on T (black). Read 1,865 on D under hairline. Here the (black) tangent scale has been used as though it were a C scale to perform a multiplication. Part (b) could have been solved another way:

$$\text{kvar} = (\text{kva}) \sin \Theta = 4,415 \sin 25° = 1,865$$

Here the S scale has been used like a C scale, for multiplication.

Another example will further illustrate the complete consistency possible in viewing the trigonometric scales as equivalent to C or CI scales.

**Example:** During a zero power factor test on an alternator, a phase angle of 89° was actually attained. The power delivered by the machine was 520 kw when operated at rated current and voltage. Find (a) the rated kva and (b) the reactive kva drawn during the test.

**Solution:**

$$\text{(a)} \quad \text{kva} = \frac{\text{kw}}{\cos \theta} = \frac{520}{\cos 89°} = 520 \sec 89° = 29{,}800.$$

In this solution the slide rule operator observes that his cosine scale ends at 84.27°. He finds instead a scale Sec T (red) covering this region. In place of dividing by cos 89°, he multiplies by sec 89°, since $1/\cos \theta = \sec \theta$. It is interesting to note that the settings employed are identical with the settings which would be required to divide by cos 89° had the secant scale been made black and called "cosine." This scale is made red and called "secant" in the design of the slide rule because it is desirable to utilize the same scale for tangents. The tangent and the secant are nearly equal in this range, and the tangent scale requires the red color.

$$\text{(b)} \quad \text{kvars} = (\text{kw}) \tan \theta = 520 \tan 89° = 29{,}800$$

Here it is observed that the same setting is used as in (a), since for angles near 90° tan θ is approximately equal to sec θ.

## THEORY AND PROCEDURES

In Electrical Engineering the principal applications will be in the solution of alternating current problems where it is necessary to make frequent conversions between the polar and the rectangular forms of the phasor (often but improperly called vector) quantities. In Electrical Engineering, these quantities are symbolized in the following two forms:

$$\begin{array}{ccc}
\text{Polar Form} & & \text{Rectangular Form} \\
A \underline{|\theta} & = & a + jb
\end{array} \qquad (1)$$

The angle θ may have any value from zero to 360 degrees and quite frequently is close to zero degrees or to 90 degrees. The process of conversion from polar to rectangular form will be discussed first.

## I. Polar Phasor to Rectangular Phasor.

For purposes of illustration, let the phasor be an impedance

$$Z\underline{|\Theta} = R + jX \qquad (2)$$

Where:    Z is magnitude in ohms;
            Θ is phase angle in degrees;
            R is resistance in ohms;
            j is $\sqrt{-1}$, called in mathematics **i**;
            X is reactance in ohms.

The problem is: given Z and Θ, to find R and X. The relations are
Graphically:

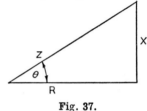

Fig. 37.

Analytically:

$$Z\underline{|\Theta} = Z \cos \Theta + jZ \sin \Theta \qquad (3)$$

The solution takes the form:

$$R = Z \cos \Theta \qquad X = Z \sin \Theta \qquad (4)$$

which for convenience is usually applied in one of the following equivalent forms:

$$R = X/\tan \Theta \qquad X = Z \sin \Theta \qquad (5)$$
$$R = Z \cos \Theta \qquad X = R \tan \Theta \qquad (6)$$

Equation (4), while simple to visualize, requires additional labor under certain circumstances. Equations (5) and (6) cover all situations with equal economy of effort.

Equations (5) and (6) suggest the following rules:

(**A**) When Θ < 45°, use (5). First find X = Z sin Θ, then divide this result by tan Θ to get R. For Example:

$$1.2\underline{|7°} = 1.2 \sin 7°/\tan 7° + j\ 1.2 \sin 7° = 1.19 + j\ 0.1462$$

(**B**) When Θ > 45°, use (6). First find R = Z cos Θ, then multiply this result by tan Θ to get X. For example:

$$1.2\underline{|70°} = 1.2 \cos 70° + j\ (1.2 \cos 70°) \tan 70° = 0.410 + j\ 1.128$$

The reader, having recognized that the trigonometric scales are used exactly as C or CI scales for multiplication and division, will check the above examples without difficulty. He will observe that such problems are solved with three motions: set slide, set hairline, set slide. As a check on proper procedure, he should have worked as follows:

**Procedure A:** Note that the angle is less than 45°. Therefore, find the imaginary component first. Set the index of C to 1.2 on D; set the hairline to 7° on S; read X = 0.1462 under hairline on D; move slide to bring 7° on T (black) under hairline; read R = 1.19 on D under index of C.

**Procedure B:** Note angle is greater than 45°. Therefore, find real component first. Set the index of C to 1.2 on D; set the hairline to 70° on Cos; read R = 0.410 under hairline on D; move slide to bring 70° on T (red) under hairline; read X = 1.128 on D under index of C.

In practice, procedures A and B are almost identical. It is only necessary to watch the first multiplication, using the S scale in the one case and the Cos scale in the other.

### EXERCISES

Convert the following polar form phasors to rectangular form:

| | |
|---|---|
| 199. $1.2 \underline{\lfloor 44°}$ | 205. $1.2 \underline{\lfloor 46°}$ |
| 200. $9 \underline{\lfloor 30°}$ | 206. $9 \underline{\lfloor 60°}$ |
| 201. $9 \underline{\lfloor -30°}$ | 207. $9 \underline{\lfloor -60°}$ |
| 202. $0.02 \underline{\lfloor 29.2°}$ | 208. $0.02 \underline{\lfloor 60.8°}$ |
| 203. $0.02 \underline{\lfloor -29.2°}$ | 209. $0.02 \underline{\lfloor -60.8°}$ |
| 204. $36.2 \underline{\lfloor 10°}$ | 210. $36.2 \underline{\lfloor 80°}$ |

Rules A and B may now be summarized in a single inclusive rule:

**(C)** To convert a polar phasor to complex form, find first the smaller component by multiplying Z by sin θ or cos θ as the case may require; then divide or multiply by tan θ as the case may require.

The application of Rule C is extremely easy to master since the slide rule settings take the same form whether θ is less than or greater than 45°. The reader should repeat exercises (199) to (210) with rule C in mind. The slide rule settings will be: Set an index of C to Z on D. Set hairline to sin θ (θ < 45°) or to cos θ (θ > 45°). Read X (θ < 45°) or R (θ > 45°) on D under hairline. Move slide until θ on T (black or red), is under hairline. Read R (θ < 45°) or X (θ > 45°) on D at an index of C.

Exercises (199) to (210) included only angles between 5.73° and 84.27°. There is no difficulty in placing the decimal point in these cases since within this range all components, whether real or imaginary, must lie between 0.1 Z and 1.0 Z. The next step is to extend the range to very small angles.

**Polar Phasor to Rectangular Phasor for Angles less than 5.73°.** The concepts expressed in rule C may be applied unchanged. Hence, find the short side by multiplying Z by sin θ, using angles on scale ST (black). However, when the second step is taken, i.e., the division of X by tan θ, it will be apparent that the result will be R = Z. That is to say, for angles less than 5.73°, the real or resistive component of Z is equal to Z. It is only necessary, then, to calculate X, the short side of the triangle.

Example:

$$1.2 \underline{|5°} = 1.2 + j\ 1.2 \sin 5° = 1.2 + j\ 0.1047$$

It should be remembered that the range of the ST scale is from 0.01 on the left to 0.1 on the right. Hence, the X component lies between 0.01 Z and 0.1 Z.

The lower limit of ST in terms of angle is 0.573°, found near the left end. The nature of this scale is such that we can begin again at the right end with 0.573° and range on down to 0.0573° at the left end, merely by moving the decimal point one place to the left, in both θ and sin θ. In this way, the conversion from polar form to rectangular form may be made for angles as near zero as we please. This cyclic feature of the ST scale results from the fact that it is based on the approximation (valid to slide rule accuracy for angles less than 5.73°) that

$$θ\ (\text{in radians}) = \sin θ = \tan θ$$

The scale gives correct values of θ in radians when used with the C scale. Consequently, there is a small but innocuous error in the values of sin θ and tan θ as read from the C scale for angles near the 5.73° limit of ST. The reader should insure his own confidence in the ST scale by comparing values of sin θ and tan θ taken from it with corresponding values found in trigonometric tables.

**Examples:** (The first is repeated for comparison)

$$1.2 \underline{|5°} = 1.2 + j\ 1.2 \sin 5° = 1.2 + j\ 0.1047$$
$$1.2 \underline{|0.7°} = 1.2 + j\ 1.2 \sin 0.7° = 1.2 + j\ 0.01467$$
$$1.2 \underline{|0.5°} = 1.2 + j\ 1.2 \sin 0.5° = 1.2 + j\ 0.01047$$
$$1.2 \underline{|0.07°} = 1.2 + j\ 1.2 \sin 0.07° = 1.2 + j\ 0.001467,\ \text{etc.}$$

The decimal point in X is moved to the left as many places as the decimal point in θ is moved. Another way of expressing this relationship is—the range of the ST scale is multiplied by $10^{-1}$ every time the decimal point is moved one place to the left in the angular markings of this scale.

## EXERCISES

Convert to complex form:

211. $4,200 | 2.5°$
212. $4,200 | 0.25°$
213. $4,200 | 0.025°$

**Polar Phasor to Rectangular Phasor for Angles greater than 84.27°.** Here again, the long side of the triangle, in this case X, is to be taken equal to Z. The short side is calculated according to Rule C from:

$$R = Z \cos \Theta = Z/\sec \Theta$$

**Example:**

$$9 | 88° = 9/\sec 88° + j\, 9 = 0.314 + j\, 9$$

Here the setting employed is: Right index of slide to 9; hairline to 88° on Sec T (red); read R = 0.314 under hairline on C. The secant scale is essentially a CI scale, hence it is employed for division like a CI scale. In other words, the proper view point to hold for angles greater than 84.27° is still to find the real component by multiplying Z by cos Θ. When the attempt is made on the slide rule, a secant scale is found in place of a cosine scale in this range of angles. So we divide by sec Θ as the equivalent of multiplying by cosine Θ.

The cosine scale covers the range of angles from 0° to 84.26° and of cosines from 1.0 to 0.1. The left end values of 84.26° and cosine = 0.1, are equivalent to 84.26° and secant = 10.0. The Sec T (red) scale begins with 84.27° at its right end and extends to 89.427° and secant = 100.0 (cosine = 0.01) at the left end. Like the ST scale, this scale can be used repeatedly for angles nearer and nearer to 90°. For each recycling, the fractional part 427 is to be moved one decimal place to the right and the vacated place replaced by a nine (9) as summarized in the following table:

Sec T (red) Scale:

|  | Left end | Right end |
|---|---|---|
| Given range: | sec 89.427° = 100 | sec 84.27° = 10.0 |
| Second range: | sec 89.9427° = 1000 | sec 89.427° = 100 |
| Third range: | sec 89.99427° = 10000 | sec 89.9427° = 1000 |
| etc. | | |

**Examples:**

$1.2 | \underline{85°} = 1.2/\sec 85° + j\ 1.2 = 0.1047 + j\ 1.2$

$1.2 | \underline{89.3°} = 1.2/\sec 89.3° + j\ 1.2 = 0.01466 + j\ 1.2$

$1.2 | \underline{89.5°} = 1.2/\sec 89.5° + j\ 1.2 = 0.01047 + j\ 1.2$

$1.2 | \underline{89.93°} = 1.2/\sec 89.93° + j\ 1.2 = 0.001466 + j\ 1.2$

etc.

## EXERCISES

Convert to complex form:

214.  $4,200 | \underline{87.5°}$

215.  $4,200 | \underline{89.75°}$

216.  $4,200 | \underline{89.975°}$

**Phasors Not in First Quadrant.** (Conversion from polar to rectangular form.) In electrical problems phasors frequently appear at angles greater than 90°, i.e., in the second, third, and fourth quadrants. Line potential differences and currents at various points along a transmission line may lag several quadrants behind the input voltage. Transfer impedances may have any angle whatever. (A transfer impedance is defined as the ratio of a source potential difference applied in one branch of a network to the current in some other branch.) Such problems are brought within the scope of the preceding discussion of the first quadrant by the method illustrated in the following example.

Example 1.

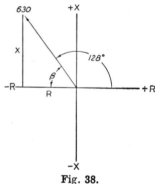

Fig. 38.

A transfer impedance is known in polar form as 630 ohms at angle 128°. Find its real and reactive components.

The recommended procedure is to draw a sketch in polar form as shown in the diagram. Calculate the angle $\beta$, the smaller angle made by the phasor with the horizontal axis.

Determine R and X by the methods explained for the first quadrant and give these components the proper sign as indicated in the sketch.

$\beta = 180° - 128° = 52°$

$630 | \underline{52°} = 630 \cos 52° + j(630 \cos 52°)(\tan 52°) = 388 + j\ 497$

$630 | \underline{128°} = -388 + j\ 497$

Example 2.

$630\underline{|218°} = R + jX$. Find R and X.

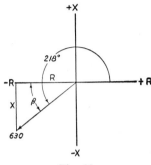

Fig. 39.

$\beta = 218° - 180° = 38°$

$630\underline{|38°} = (630 \sin 38°)/\tan 38° + j\,630 \sin 38° = 497 + j\,388$

$630\underline{|218°} = -497 - j\,388$

Example 3.

$630\underline{|308°} = R + jX$. Find R and X.

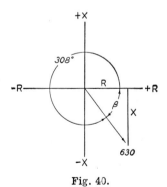

Fig. 40.

$\beta = 360° - 308° = 52°$

$630\underline{|52°} = 630 \cos 52° + j(630 \cos 52°) \tan 52° = 388 + j\,497$

$630\underline{|308°} = 388 - j\,497$

### EXERCISES

Convert the following phasors to complex form:

217. 220 $\underline{|62°}$

218. 220 $\underline{|152°}$

219. 220 $\underline{|242°}$

220. 220 $\underline{|332°}$

221. 220 $\underline{|-28°}$

## II. Rectangular Phasor to Polar Phasor.

The problem is the inverse of that stated at the beginning of section **I**, and will be handled by the same relations, i.e., equations (5) and (6), rearranged as follows:

$$X/R = \tan \theta/1 = \tan \theta/\tan 45°; \quad Z = X/\sin \theta \qquad (7)$$

$$R/X = 1/\tan \theta = \tan 45°/\tan \theta; \quad Z = R/\cos \theta \qquad (8)$$

Equation (7) is to be used when $\theta < 45°$.

Equation (8) is to be used when $\theta > 45°$.

Two examples carried through in parallel form will illustrate the two cases:

To find $Z\underline{|\theta}$ when

$R + jX = 4.33 + j\ 2.5$

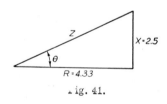

ᴵig. 41.

$R + jX = 2.5 + j\ 4.33$

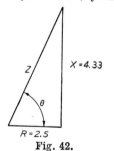

**Fig. 42.**

Find $\theta$ using the proportion

$\qquad X/R = \tan \theta/\tan 45°$

Settings: Hairline to 2.5 on D. Index of slide to 4.33.

The hairline is now located at $60°/30°$ on T; choose $\theta = 30°$ because $X < R$.

Find $Z$ using $Z = X/\sin \theta$.

Settings: The hairline is already on X on the D scale. Move slide to bring sin 30° under hairline. Read $Z = 5$ on D under index of slide.

Find $\theta$ using the proportion

$\qquad R/X = \tan 45°/\tan \theta$

Settings: Hairline to 2.5. Index of slide to 4.33.

The hairline is now located at $60°/30°$ on T; choose $\theta = 60°$ because $X > R$.

Find $Z$ using $Z = R/\cos \theta$.

Settings: The hairline is already on R on the D scale. Move slide to bring cos 30° under hairline. Read $Z = 5$ on D under index of slide.

If the reader will carry out the operations just described, he will see that *the two cases resulted in identical slide rule settings* throughout. Differences appear only in the interpretation of the settings. Thus, to determine the angle, a choice had to be made between 30° and its complement, 60°. This choice should be made solely as a result of visualization of the triangle: If $X < R$, choose the smaller angle. If $X > R$, choose the larger angle.

Again, in finding Z after θ was known, a choice had to be made between dividing the hairline setting by sin θ or by cos θ. Again, the choice is made by visualizing the trigonometry involved: If hairline is on X, divide by sin θ, (sin 30°) If hairline is on R, divide by cos θ, (cos 60°) Since sin 30° = cos 60°, these two settings were identical. The reader is now in a position to appreciate the following:

**Rule D:** To find $Z \underline{|\theta}$ when the two components R and X are given:

1. Set the hairline to the *smaller* component on D.

2. Set an index of the slide to the *larger* component on D. Under the hairline, read the angle on T (black or red) selecting the proper angle by visualization of the triangle.

3. Leaving the hairline on X or on R as the case may be, divide X by sin θ or R by cos θ to get Z. (Bearing in mind that the S and Cos scales are fundamentally C scales the user can readily determine how to perform the division.)

### Examples:

$0.863 + j\ 0.834 = 1.20\underline{|44°}$     $1.19 + j\ 0.1462 = 1.20\underline{|7°}$

$0.411 + j\ 1.128 = 1.20\underline{|70°}$     $0.1253 + j\ 1.193 = 1.20\underline{|84°}$

### EXERCISES

Convert the following phasors to polar form:

222. $0.863 + j\ 0.834$       228. $0.834 + j\ 0.863$

223. $7.8 + j\ 4.5$       229. $4.5 + j\ 7.8$

224. $7.8 - j\ 4.5$       230. $4.5 - j\ 7.8$

225. $0.01745 + j\ 0.00976$       231. $0.00976 + j\ 0.01745$

226. $0.01745 - j\ 0.00976$       232. $6.29 + j\ 35.65$

227. $35.65 + j\ 6.29$

**Rectangular Phasor to Polar Phasor for Small and for Large Angles.** In the foregoing problems the ratio $X/R = \tan \theta$ or $R/X = 1/\tan \theta$ is limited to the range 1.0 to 10.0, corresponding to angles between 5.71° and 84.29°. It is important to extend the range toward 0° and 90°. The slide rule user must be constantly alert for the following cases:

When $X/R < 0.1$, the angle must be read on ST instead of on T.

When $R/X < 0.1$, the angle must be read on Sec T (red) instead of on T (red).

In either case the magnitude of $Z$ is taken equal to the larger of the two components.

**Example 1.**  $1.2 + j\,0.1047 = 1.2 \underline{|5°}$

Here $\theta = 5°$ is read from the ST scale since $0.01R < X < 0.1\,R$, indicating that $0.01 < \tan \theta < 0.1$. The highest range of ST is from 0.01 to 0.1. For all values of $\theta$ on the ST scale, the approximation is made that $\sin \theta = \tan \theta$. Therefore, $Z$ equals the larger component, 1.2.

**Example 2.**  $1.2 + j\,0.01466 = 1.2 \underline{|0.7°}$

Here again $0.01\,R < X < 0.1\,R$, hence the ST scale is read without change of decimal point. This angle is near the end of what might be called a first cycle over ST.

**Example 3.**  $1.2 + j\,0.01047 = 1.2 \underline{|0.5°}$

Here $0.001\,R < X < 0.01\,R$. Hence $\theta$ is read from the ST scale but with the decimal point moved one place to left. This angle is in and near the beginning of a second cycle over ST.

**Example 4.**  $1.2 + j\,0.001466 = 1.2 \underline{|0.07°}$

This is similar to example 3. The angle is in and near the end of the second cycle over ST.

**Example 5.**  $1.2 + j\,0.001047 = 1.2 \underline{|0.05°}$

Here the ST scale decimal points will be moved two places to the left. This angle is in and near the beginning of a third cycle over ST.

**Example 6.**  $1.2 + j\,0.0001466 = 1.2 \underline{|0.007°}$

In this example the ST scale decimal points will again be moved two places to the left. This angle is in and near the end of a third cycle over ST.

**Example 7.**   $0.1047 + j\ 1.2 = 1.2 \underline{|85°}$

In examples 1 to 6, X < R, requiring the use of ST. Here X > R which requires the use of Sec T (red). Angles are read without change of decimal point when 0.01 X < R < 0.1 X. In example 7 the angle is in and near the beginning of a first cycle over Sec T (red) approaching 90°.

**Example 8.**   $0.01466 + j\ 1.2 = 1.2 \underline{|89.3°}$

This is similar to example 7. The angle is in and near the end of a first cycle over Sec T (red), approaching 90°.

**Example 9.**   $0.01047 + j\ 1.2 = 1.2 \underline{|89.5°}$

Here the hairline will be near the beginning of a second cycle over Sec T (red).   In example 7 we were 5° short of 90°.   Here we are 0.5° short of 90°.

**Example 10.**   $0.001466 + j\ 1.2 = 1.2 \underline{|89.93°}$

In example 10 the hairline will be near the end of a second cycle over Sec T (red).   In example 8 we were 0.7° short of 90°.   Here we are 0.07° short of 90°.

## EXERCISES

Convert the following phasors to polar form:

|  |  |
|---|---|
| 233. 4,200 + j 183.2 | 237. 183.2 + j 4,200 |
| 234. 4,200 + j 18.32 | 238. 18.32 + j 4,200 |
| 235. 4,200 + j 1.832 | 239. 1.832 + j 4,200 |
| 236. 0.314 + j 9 | |

For rectangular form to polar form for angles not in the first quadrant, the reader should refer back to the corresponding problem in conversion from polar form to rectangular form. The angle $\beta$ is to be found by the method just developed. Inspection of the diagram will then reveal how to find Θ.

## EXERCISES

Convert the following phasors to polar form:

|  |  |
|---|---|
| 240. 103.3 + j 194.2 | 242. −103.3 − j 194.2 |
| 241. −194.2 + j 103.3 | 243. 194.2 − j 103.3 |

# ANSWERS TO EXERCISES

## Multiplication

1. 7.25   Use D and CI scales, exercises 1 to 6.
2. 4.48
3. 20.8
4. 3.45
5. 23.4
6. 30.5
7. 25.8   Use DF and CIF scales, exercises 7 to 12.
8. 1.967
9. 75.2
10. 68.2
11. 46.6
12. 32.3
13. 108.7   Use D and CI scales or DF and CIF, exercises 13 to 18.
14. 224
15. 1,990
16. 605
17. 8,370
18. 4,050

## Division

19. 3.02   Use D and C scales, exercises 19 to 24.
20. 2.89
21. 2.84
22. 23.3
23. 23.4
24. 4.48
25. 4.27   Use DF and CF scales, exercises 25 to 30.
26. 8.14
27. 0.0650
28. 0.444
29. 43.3
30. 20.6
31. 1.431   Use D and C scales or DF and CF, exercises 31 to 36.
32. 1.670
33. 2.11
34. 0.840
35. 7.87
36. 184.0

## Products of a Series of Factors

37. 121.4
38. 255
39. 5,520,000
40. 0.303
41. 0.506
42. 2.77
43. 0.611
44. 0.0608
45. 0.1644
46. 0.805

## A Single Factor Multiplied by a Series of Numbers

47. 368; 774; 1,018; 1,440; 1,734; 2,200; 2,550; 2,580; 3,070.
48. 7.04; 3.34; 2.18; 1.718; 1.266; 1.120; 0.915; 0.820; 0.769.

## Proportion

49. 3.48
50. 1.328
51. 3.97
52. 181.2
53. 6.09

## Quadratic Equations

54. −34.0 and −0.53
55. 19.5 and 1.64
56. 25.0 and −4.8
57. −23.6 and −17.8
58. 6.6 and 4.55

## Square Roots and Squares

59. 2.45
60. 5.196
61. 30.4
62. 35.57
63. 267.4
64. 905
65. 1,404
66. 7,140
67. 416
68. 51,100
69. 1,145,000
70. 15,730
71. 0.722
72. 0.00884
73. 0.0000578
74. 0.0000000246
75. 0.651
76. 0.2958
77. 0.0851
78. 0.003065

## Areas of Circles

79.   0.0492; 0.1105; 0.1963; 0.307; 0.602; 0.785.

## Cube Root and Cubes

80.   1817
81.   2.88
82.   6.46
83.   1.1.98
84.   30.7
85.   82.4
86.   32.8
87.   6,900
88.   422,000,000
89.   0.684
90.   0.345
91.   0.1957
92.   0.0147
93.   0.0000467
94.   0.000000111

## Powers of e

95.   148; 1.492; 1.0304; 1.00804.
96.   0.0183; 0.407; 0.9287; 0.99442.

## Reciprocals

97.   0.000117; 0.00133; 0.0156; 0.1175; 1.0515; 13.25; 178; 7,100.

## Hyperbolic Functions

98.   0.201
99.   10.02
100.   1.103
101.   0.336
102.   0.971
103.   2.98
104.   0.59
105.   1.99
106.   0.78
107.   1.57
108.   0.31

## Powers of Numbers

109.   1.00525
110.   1.1172
111.   6.07
112.   18.2
113.   0.99493
114.   0.717
115.   0.0058
116.   0.578
117.   0.0109
118.   0.421
119.   1.387
120.   1.00915

## Exponential Equations

121. 1.267
122. 3.62
123. 5.50
124. 4.74

## Natural Trigonometric Functions

125. 0.970
126. 0.814
127. 0.266
128. 0.0157
129. 0.0673
130. 0.824
131. 0.264
132. 0.1132
133. 0.281
134. 1.163
135. 4.51
136. 8.85
137. 81.8
138. 35.8
139. 0.0419

## Solution of Triangles

140. $A = 21.7°$; $B = 68.3°$; $c = 24.3'$.
141. $a = 53.8'$; $c = 54.9'$.
142. $A = 25.6°$; $B = 45.8°$; $C = 108.6°$.

## Complex Numbers

143. $x = 9.87$; $y = 13.60$.
144. $x = 18.71$; $y = 9.54$.
145. $16.6 \, e^{j.32.4°}$.

## Applications to Civil Engineering

146. (a) 10,200 cu. ft.; (b) 10,060 cu. ft.
147. 438.88 ft.
148. 243 ft.; N. 22.77° W.
149. 137.4 ft.
150. 220 ft.
151. (a) $V = 95.2$ ft.; $H = 526$ ft.
     (b) $V = 27.8$ ft.; $H = 211$ ft.
     (c) $V = 135.5$ ft.; $H = 378$ ft.
152. (a) $R = 848$ ft.; $D = 6.76°$; $I = 14.1°$.
     (b) $R = 481$ ft.; $D = 11.94°$; $I = 17.58°$.
     (c) $R = 373$ ft.; $D = 15.40°$; $I = 9.47°$.
153. (a) $C = 5'\text{-}2\frac{1}{8}''$; $R = 7\frac{3}{16}''$.
     (b) $C = 11'\text{-}6''$; $R = 10\frac{1}{2}''$.
     (c) $C = 15'\text{-}6\frac{1}{8}''$; $R = 3\frac{29}{32}''$.
154. (a) $R = 10\frac{13}{16}''$.
     (b) $R = 11\frac{1}{8}''$.
     (c) $R = 5\frac{7}{8}''$.

155. Fig. (a)—Stress A = 11,660# Tens.; Stress B = 8,940# Compr.
     Fig. (b)—A = 11,350# Compr.; B = 11,550# Compr.; C = 11,550# Compr.;
          D = 13,680# Compr.;     E = 8,030# Tens.;     F = 8,030# Tens.;
          G = 9,670# Tens.;       H = 9,670# Tens.;     I = 4,500# Tens.;
          J = 5,000# Tens.;  K = 0;  L = 2,640# Tens.;  M = 7,800# Tens.
156. $R_L$ = 19,430#; $R_R$ = 14,330#. Moments in foot pounds are 77,700; 129,800;
     152,000; 134,900; and 86,000 at points 1, 2, 3, 4, and 5 respectively. Maxi-
     mum bending stress is 16,900#/sq. in.
157. x = 9.40 in.; $f_c$ = 1,070#/sq. in.; $f_s$ = 20,000#/sq. in.
158. y = 6 (cosh 0.0195 × −1); H = 316,000#; V = 343,000#; T = 466,000#.
159. $p_1$ = 680#/sq. ft.; $p_2$ = 4,600#/sq. ft.

## Applications to Mechanical Engineering

160. 792 deg. R.
161. 4.15 psia
162. 3.68 psia
163. 1.36
164. 44.8 btu
165. 4.81 ft³
166. 0.139 btu/deg. R.
167. −81.1 btu
168. 51.6 btu/lb.
169. −1.935 btu/deg. R.
170. 230 psia
171. 2820 btu/hr.
172. 1520 btu/hr. F ft²
173. 416 F, 92 F, 4.1 ft²
174. 96.8 F
175. 2710 btu/hr.
176. 13.25 in.⁴; 1.415 in.
177. 103.6 in.⁴; 2.67 in.
178. 237.7 in.
179. 147.7°; 2.58 radians; 734 lbs.; 438 lbs.
180. 0.729 ft.; 727 ft/min.; 0.0214 ft; 183 ft/min.

## Applications to Electrical Engineering

181. 12.2 ohms
182. 0.0410 ohms
183. 1,114,000 C.M.
184. 3.59 watts
185. 45.1 watts
186. 300 ohms
187. 126.7 $\mu\mu$f
188. 293.7 volts
189. 0.99960
190. 45,700 C.M.
191. 3.01 d. b. loss
192. 47 d.b.
193. 22.2 d.b. loss
194. 1.84 (10)⁻⁴ amps.
195. 6.75 (10)⁻⁵ amps.
196. 4.90 (10)⁻⁴ amps.
197. 1.048 (10)⁻⁵
198. 0.0339 amps.

| | |
|---|---|
| 199. | 0.863 + j 0.834 |
| 200. | 7.80 + j 4.50 |
| 201. | 7.80 − j 4.50 |
| 202. | 0.01745 + j 0.00976 |
| 203. | 0.01745 − j 0.00976 |
| 204. | 35.6 + j 6.29 |
| 205. | 0.834 + j 0.863 |
| 206. | 4.50 + j 7.80 |
| 207. | 4.50 − j 7.80 |
| 208. | 0.00976 + j 0.01745 |
| 209. | 0.00976 − j 0.01745 |
| 210. | 6.29 + j 35.6 |
| 211. | 4,200 + j 183.2 |
| 212. | 4,200 + j 18.32 |
| 213. | 4,200 + j 1.832 |
| 214. | 183.2 + j 4,200 |
| 215. | 18.32 + j 4,200 |
| 216. | 1.832 + j 4,200 |
| 217. | 103.3 + j 194.2 |
| 218. | −194.2 + j 103.3 |
| 219. | −103.3 − j 194.2 |
| 220. | 194.2 − j 103.3 |
| 221. | 194.2 − j 103.3 |
| 222. | 1.2 $\underline{/44°}$ |
| 223. | 9.0 $\underline{/30°}$ |
| 224. | 9.0 $\underline{/-30°}$ |
| 225. | 0.02 $\underline{/29.22°}$ |
| 226. | 0.02 $\underline{/-29.22°}$ |
| 227. | 36.2 $\underline{/10°}$ |
| 228. | 1.2 $\underline{/46°}$ |
| 229. | 9$\underline{/60°}$ |
| 230. | 9$\underline{/-60°}$ |
| 231. | 0.02 $\underline{/60.8°}$ |
| 232. | 36.2 $\underline{/80°}$ |
| 233. | 4,200 $\underline{/2.5°}$ |
| 234. | 4,200 $\underline{/0.25°}$ |
| 235. | 4,200 $\underline{/0.025°}$ |
| 236. | 9 $\underline{/88°}$ |
| 237. | 4,200 $\underline{/87.5°}$ |
| 238. | 4,200 $\underline{/89.75°}$ |
| 239. | 4,200 $\underline{/89.975°}$ |
| 240. | 220 $\underline{/62°}$ |
| 241. | 220 $\underline{/152°}$ |
| 242. | 220 $\underline{/242°}$ |
| 243. | 220 $\underline{/332°}$ |